ELECTRIC MOTORS
SELECTING, PROTECTING AND SERVICING

No. 2663
$19.95

ELECTRIC MOTORS
SELECTING, PROTECTING AND SERVICING

AMERICAN ASSOCIATION FOR VOCATIONAL
INSTRUCTIONAL MATERIALS (AAVIM)

 TAB BOOKS Inc.
Blue Ridge Summit, PA 17214

The American Association for Vocational Instructional Materials (AAVIM) is a non-profit national institute.

The institute is a cooperative effort of universities, colleges and divisions of vocational and technical education in the United States and Canada to provide for excellence in instructional materials.

Direction is given by a representative from each of the states, provinces and territories. AAVIM also works closely with teacher organizations, government agencies and industry.

DIRECTOR

W. Harold Parady, Executive Director, AAVIM

REVISION

James M. Allison, Assoc. Prof., Agricultural Engineering Division, University of Georgia and

J. Howard Turner, Editor and Coordinator, AAVIM

ART DIRECTOR

George W. Smith, Jr., Art Director, AAVIM

GRAPHIC DESIGN

James E. Wren, Media Development Specialist, AAVIM

ACKNOWLEDGMENTS

This publication was initially prepared in 1959 by **Robert H. Brown,** Professor and Chairman, Agricultural Engineering Center, **G. E. Henderson,** former Executive Director, AAVIM and Professor Emeritus, Agricultural Engineering, University of Georgia and **C. E. Turner,** formerly of the University of Georgia.

See pages 117-119 for other acknowledgments.

SECOND PRINTING

The fifth edition of *Electric Motors* was revised, copyrighted, and published in 1982 by AAVIM.

Library of Congress Cataloging in Publication Data

Main entry under title:

Electric motors.

    Bibliography: p.
    Includes index.
    1. Electric motors, Alternating current.
    I. American Association for Vocational Instructional
Materials.
TK2781.E46   1986   621.46′2   85-32110
ISBN 0-8306-2163-6
ISBN 0-8306-0463-4 (pbk.)

Cover photograph courtesy of Reliance Electric Company, Athens, Georgia.

Contents

Preface

From this book you will develop the knowledge and skills needed in selecting electric motors, starters (overload protective devices), and drives. It is especially designed for persons in agriculture and industry where replacement motors are required.

ELECTRIC MOTORS
SELECTING, PROTECTING AND SERVICING

Introduction

This book is prepared to help you select the electric motor that is best suited to drive your equipment. The information given is important because electric motors are used to power practically all types of equipment in homes, businesses and factories (Fig. 1). In fact, the average home, farm, or small industry may have 20 or more electric motors.

One of the main reasons for the popularity of electric motors is their ability to do work. For example, a single .8 kW (1 hp) motor can do as much work as 8 to 10 men (Fig. 2). In addition, electric motors have many advantages over other types of power. Some of these advantages are as follows:

- Reasonable in first cost.
- Relatively inexpensive to operate.
- Long in life (20 to 30 years, with proper care).
- Simple to operate.
- Quiet.
- Safe.
- High efficiency.
- Capable of withstanding temporary overloads.
- Capable of being automatically and remotely controlled.
- Compact.

Fig. 1. Electric motors serve mankind in many ways.

Fig. 2. An .8 kW (1 hp) electric motor can do the work of 8 to 10 persons.

- Little affected by hot or cold weather.
- No exhaust fumes.
- Very little vibration.
- Adaptable to different operating positions.
- Minimum fire hazard.
- Minimum servicing.

To profit by these many advantages, you need to have a working knowledge of the different motors, where they can be used, and their limitations. You should be able to replace them in the event of a failure. You may want to modernize hand-driven equipment or make some new application of power. To be successful in this endeavor, you must be able to select the proper motor, the proper control (protection), and the proper drive.

There are two kinds of electric motors, based on the type of current on which they operate. They are alternating current (ac) and direct current (dc). *Alternating-current* motors are the ones that operate from electric power lines. *Direct-current* motors usually operate from batteries. There are rectifiers, however, made for changing ac to dc for special applications. Since you will be dealing mostly with ac motors, they are the only ones discussed in this publication.

How to select and service the proper ac motor, control and drive is discussed under the following major headings:

    I.   Selecting Electric Motors.
   II.   Selecting Motor Overload Protective Devices.
 III.   Selecting Motor Drives.
 IV.   Servicing and Troubleshooting.

Caution! Remember to protect yourself and others against injury while working with electric motors and equipment. Follow directions given in the National Electrical Code, local codes, and the National Electrical Manufacturers' Association.

Part I

Selecting Electric Motors

Most power equipment you buy has an electric motor. For instance, when you buy a drill press, air compressor, or duplicating machine, the electric motor is already installed as part of the equipment. The only electrical information you need to know when purchasing is the type of power you have available: that is, the voltage, cycles and phase.

If you are replacing an electric motor on equipment that is already powered by an electric motor, you can assume that the motor can be removed and that it operated satisfactorily before. In this instance, you replace the motor with one of the same specifications. For this information, check the nameplate of the motor being replaced (Fig. 3). You should supply all of the nameplate information when you contact your dealer.

If you do not know what motor is needed for a piece of equipment, you will have several decisions to make regarding size, speed and type. How to make these decisions is discussed under the following headings:

A. What Size (Power) Motor to Select.
B. What Motor Speed (RPM) to Select.
C. What Motor Duty to Select.

1

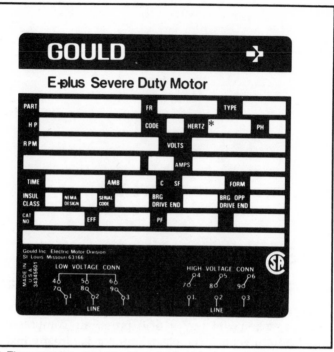

Fig. 3. The nameplate on an electric motor furnishes you with the information you need to replace the motor. The term "Hertz" now replaces the term "cycles per second."

D. What Motor Type to Select.
E. What Type of Bearings to Select.
F. What Type of Enclosure to Select.
G. What Type of Mounting Base to Select.

A. What Size (Power) Motor to Select

In selecting an electric motor of the proper size to replace another type of power, your first job is to determine how much power is needed to drive your equipment. If you get a motor that is too small for the job, you will have trouble. An overloaded motor will, if not properly protected, overheat and burn out. If it is properly protected but overloaded, the protective device will open the circuit—the power to the motor is then cut off and the motor stops. So you can see why it is important to get the proper size motor.

You are not likely to be limited by the size of motor available. Motors come in practically any size as shown in the following table:

POWER OUTPUT RATINGS OF STANDARD SIZE MOTORS	
SI* (kW)	US (hp)
.025	$^1/_{20}$
.035	
.05	
.071	$^1/_8$
.1	$^1/_6$
.14	$^1/_4$
.2	$^1/_3$
.28	$^1/_2$
.4	
.56	$^3/_4$
.8	1
1.1	$1^1/_2$
1.6	2
2.5	3
4.0	5
5.6	$7^1/_2$
8.0	10

*James W. York, "A Preview of Metric Motors," Westinghouse Electric Corporation.

Unlike internal-combustion engines, electric motors are capable of developing intermittently more than twice their rated power—the power shown on the nameplate. This is the power that the motor will develop after it has reached its full running speed.

The service factor (SF) indicates how much temporary "overload" the motor will take. For example, if a motor has a service factor of 1.25 and is rated at .746 kW (1 hp), the motor can be expected to deliver .746 kW (1 hp) × 1.25 = .932 kW (1.25 hp).

The temperature rise will also be greater when operating above rated power. For example, a motor rated to operate at 40 °C rise could be expected to operate at greater than 40 °C rise (possibly a 50 °C rise) if it was delivering .932 kW (1.25 hp).

Your second job is to determine if you have enough electrical power available from your power supplier.

Your third job is to determine if you have enough capacity in your electrical service entrance.

Once you have made these three determinations, you will be able to select the proper size motor. The information you will need is given under the following headings:

1. Effect of Equipment Power Needed on Size of Motor Selected.

2. Effect of Available Electric Power on Size of Motor Selected.

3. Effect of Service Entrance Capacity on Size of Motor Selected.

1. EFFECT OF EQUIPMENT POWER NEEDED ON SIZE OF MOTOR SELECTED

The power required to operate your equipment will determine what size motor you need. You will have one of three situations. They are as follows:

a. Replacing an Internal-Combustion Engine.
b. Installing a Motor on New Equipment.
c. Installing a Motor on Hand-Powered Equipment.

a. Replacing an Internal-Combustion Engine

If you are replacing an internal-combustion engine, you will need to consider the following questions:

• Is it a small, portable engine?
• Is it an industrial engine?
• Is it a tractor power take-off (PTO) unit?

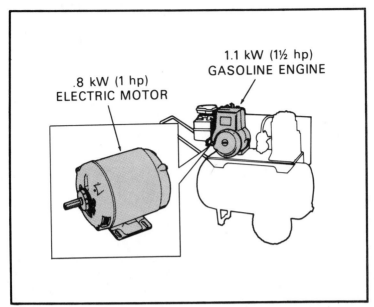

Fig. 4. A small, portable engine can usually be replaced with an electric motor of 2/3 to 3/4 its power rating.

If you are replacing a small, portable-type engine, a "rule of thumb" that is frequently used is to get a motor of approximately 2/3 to 3/4 as much power as that of the engine (Fig. 4).

Here is the reason for this difference in power. The power of an internal-combustion engine is determined under ideal conditions by the manufacturer in the test laboratory. The internal-combustion engine will not produce this much power on the job. By contrast, the power of the electric motor is measured as the amount of power that the motor will actually produce while performing a job.

If you are replacing an industrial-type engine (Fig. 5), you must understand the power rating of the engine before you can make your decision. If the industrial engine power rating is shown as "maximum brake," or "rated brake," then use the same "rule of thumb" as with the small engine. This is because the industrial engine cannot actually deliver that much power.

If the industrial engine power is shown as "kilowatts" or "continuous brake horsepower," then you should replace

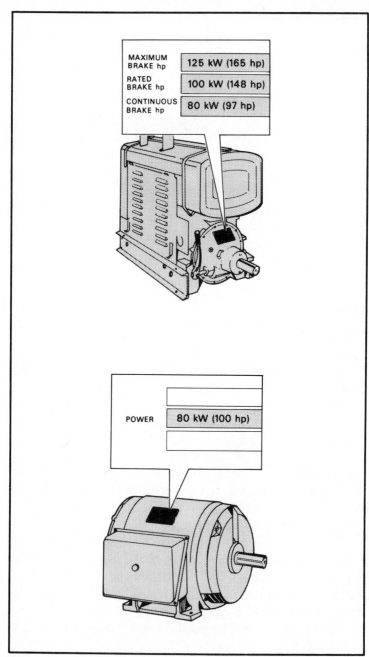

MAXIMUM BRAKE hp	125 kW (165 hp)
RATED BRAKE hp	100 kW (148 hp)
CONTINUOUS BRAKE hp	80 kW (97 hp)

POWER	80 kW (100 hp)

Fig. 5. An industrial-type engine can be replaced with an electric motor of approximately the same power as the continuous brake power of the engine.

6

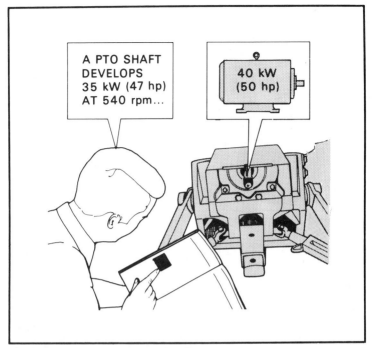

Fig. 6. A tractor PTO unit can be replaced with that of an electric motor of approximately the same power.

the engine with an electric motor of approximately the same power. This is because kilowatts or continuous brake horsepower rating of the engine is the power that it will produce while performing a job.

If you are replacing the power of a tractor PTO unit with that of an electric motor (Fig. 6), use an electric motor of approximately the same power as the PTO power rated at its standard speed. For this information, check your operator's manual.

b. Installing a Motor on New Equipment

If you are installing a motor on new equipment, or on equipment which has no power unit, your equipment manufacturer will provide a suggested motor size. The power unit size may also be indicated on the equipment nameplate or in your operator's manual (Fig. 7).

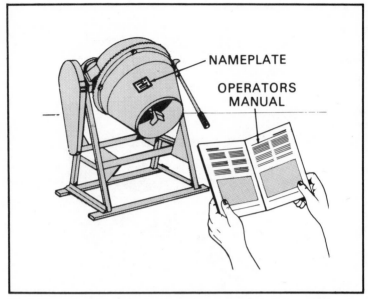

Fig. 7. The nameplate on your equipment, or your operator's manual, may give the power needed to operate the equipment.

c. Installing a Motor on Hand-Powered Equipment

If you are installing a motor on hand-powered equipment, an accepted "rule of thumb" is to use a .2 kW (1/3 hp) motor (Fig. 8). A distinct advantage is that the motor can operate the equipment continuously, whereas a person would need to stop and rest occasionally.

2. EFFECT OF AVAILABLE ELECTRIC POWER ON SIZE OF MOTOR SELECTED

Once you know what size motor you need, you can determine if your power supply is adequate for that power.

"Power supply," as discussed here, means what the power supplier has available at your premises. It may be one of the following:

a. Single-Phase, 115 or 230 volts.
b. 3-Phase, 208, 230, 460, 575, 2300, 4000 and 4600 volts.

(There is such a thing as 2-phase power, but it is not com-

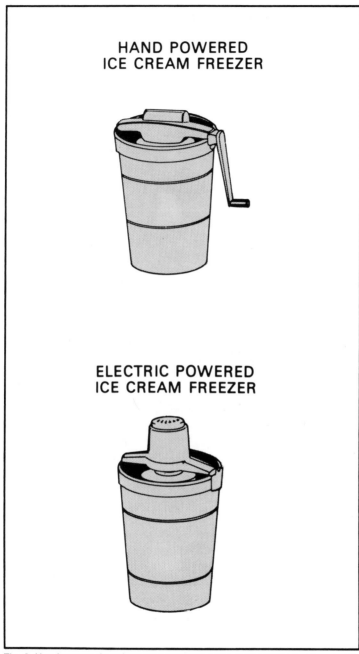

HAND POWERED
ICE CREAM FREEZER

ELECTRIC POWERED
ICE CREAM FREEZER

Fig. 8. Hand-powered equipment operated by one or two persons can usually be replaced by a .2 kW (1/3 hp) motor.

monly used. Therefore, it is not discussed here.)

To help you understand the difference between single-phase and 3-phase power, think of one man driving a tent stake; then compare this action with three men driving a tent stake (Fig. 9). Three men, hitting one after the other, can deliver three times as many licks as one man working by himself. Three-phase power is used where large quantities of power are needed. The capacity of the system is increased by a factor of 1.73.

a. Single-Phase, 115 or 230 Volts

Usually single-phase motors are limited to 5.6 kW (7 1/2 hp). Three-phase motors may be more than 746 kW (1000 hp).

Generally, electric power that is supplied to homes and to most farms and small businesses is *single-phase*. It is supplied from a power line that looks something like the one in Fig. 10. Usually, three wires extend from the pole to your electric meter. (Two wires are sometimes used for limited usage.)

It is also possible for single-phase power to be supplied from a 3-phase line. This is likely the case if you have a power line that looks something like the one in Fig. 10 except that only three wires extend from it to your premises.

Electric motors are built to operate either with single-phase power, or with 3-phase power. One motor cannot be built to operate on both.

Many single-phase motors are designed so that they may be operated on either 115V or 230V. In such motors, the connecting leads in must be positioned in the proper place to accommodate the voltage. Directions are usually given under the cover plate. If your motor is so designed, it will also be indicated on the nameplate (115/230).

Most power suppliers will permit motors of up to .28 kW (1/3 hp) on single-phase, 115-volt circuits, and from .4 kW (1/2 hp) to 4 kW (5 hp) on single-phase, 230-volt circuits (Fig. 11).

For larger motors, different power suppliers have different rules about the size of motor they will serve on single-phase power. Some will allow up to 5.6 kW (7.5 hp) or 11.2 kW (15

Fig. 9. How single-phase and 3-phase power may be compared. Think of single-phase power as one person driving a tent stake, and 3-phase power as three persons driving the same stake.

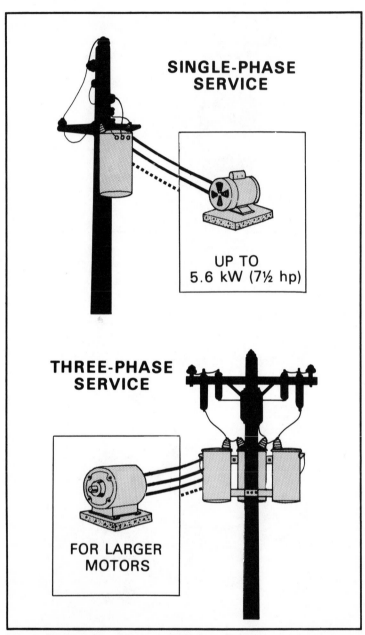

Fig. 10. Single-phase power is supplied through one transformer and two or three wires. Single-phase motors always have two wires. Three-phase service is supplied through two or three transformers and three or four wires. Three-phase motors are connected by three wires.

115 VOLTS

.28 kW
(1/3 hp)

AND....

SMALLER

230 VOLTS

.4 kW
(½ hp)

AND....

LARGER

Fig. 11. 115-volt circuits are for .28 kW (1/3 hp) motors and smaller. 230-volt circuits are used for .4 kW (1/2 hp) motors and larger. Receptacles may be used for motors of up to .8 kW (1 hp).

hp), while others may go as high as 40 kW (50 hp).

There are several reasons for limiting motor size on single-phase lines. One is that a large motor usually draws a heavy amount of current for starting, and this may dim the lights in a whole community. Second, the equipment may load the motor heavily one instant and lightly the next, causing lights to dim and brighten. There are also increased cost factors to power suppliers which must be considered when larger motors are used.

b. 3-Phase, 208, 230 Volts, or More

If 3-phase power is supplied to your premises, the power line will look something like the one shown in Fig. 10. Four wires will extend from the pole to your meter. Generally, you can use almost any size motor if 3-phase power is available. Of course, you would need to check with your power supplier for guidance.

Three-phase power is commonly used by industry for the operation of electric motors. Some of the advantages of 3-phase power over single-phase are:

- Little or no light flickering.
- 3-phase motors cost less than comparable size single-phase motors.
- 3-phase motors will last longer.

A disadvantage is that you may have to pay extra to have 3-phase lines installed.

It is possible to operate 3-phase equipment from single phase lines by using a phase converter. A phase converter is a special device that changes single-phase power to 3-phase power for motor operation (Fig. 12). Single-phase power converted to 3-phase power has many of the same advantages of regular 3-phase power. These converters will handle motors as large as 100 kW (125 hp). You can purchase one when you get your motor, or there are some instances in which the power supplier may provide the phase converter for the customer. If you get the motor from a different source, check with the phase-converter manufacturer before purchasing a motor.

There are some disadvantages of using a phase converter: many of these machines cost as much as, if not more than, the motor to be driven; many phase converters require that the load on the motor be constant; phase converters may re-

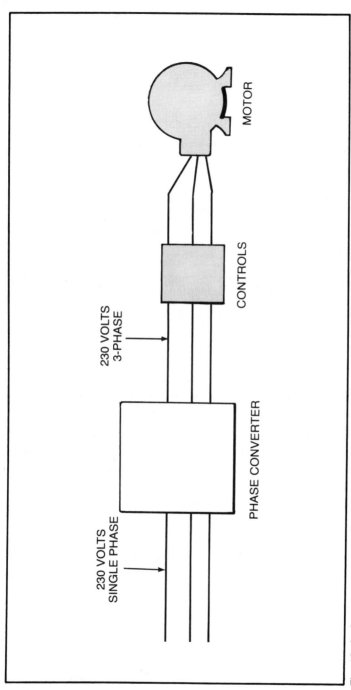

Fig. 12. A phase converter can be used on single-phase service to provide 3-phase service for motors.

15

quire more maintenance than a motor. Consult with your power supplier and equipment dealer before purchasing phase converter equipment. Follow instructions given by the manufacturer. Mismatched converters and motors may cause motor overheating. Check with the phase converter suppliers for guidance.

3. EFFECT OF SERVICE ENTRANCE CAPACITY ON SIZE OF MOTOR SELECTED

If your power supply is adequate, the next point to consider is whether or not your present service entrance is large enough. The service entrance is the main control and means of cut-off for the electrical system.

The service entrance must have about three times more amperage capacity than the amperage rating on the nameplate of the motor. This is to provide the extra amperage capacity necessary to start the motor. If your service entrance is too small for your motor, a safety device—fuse or circuit breaker in the service entrance switch—will disconnect the motor before it gets started.

Figure 13 shows what size motors may be used with different size service entrances, providing no other major load is being served. You can see that for motors of .28 kW (1/3 hp) or less, there is no problem. On motors of .4 kW (1/2 hp) or more, the service entrance must be large enough to provide adequate current (amperage) capacity and 230 volts.

If you have a service entrance of the size shown in Fig. 13, compare your motor size with the service entrance recommended. If your motor is larger than the recommended size, you must install a larger, or a separate, service entrance. In many cases, there is only one main service entrance to serve several buildings (Fig. 14). For example, suppose a 60-ampere service entrance is in use. If it is already serving an electric range, it is very doubtful if a 4-kW (5 hp) electric motor could be used satisfactorily without overloading the service entrance and blowing the main fuses.

A much better arrangement is to use a central distribution point to serve a service entrance in each main building

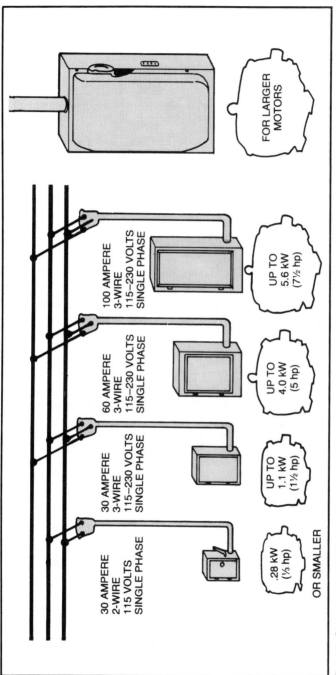

FOR LARGER MOTORS

100 AMPERE
3-WIRE
115–230 VOLTS
SINGLE PHASE

UP TO
5.6 kW
(7½ hp)

60 AMPERE
3-WIRE
115–230 VOLTS
SINGLE PHASE

UP TO
4.0 kW
(5 hp)

30 AMPERE
3-WIRE
115–230 VOLTS
SINGLE PHASE

UP TO
1.1 kW
(1½ hp)

30 AMPERE
2-WIRE
115 VOLTS
SINGLE PHASE

.28 kW
(⅓ hp)
OR SMALLER

Fig. 13. Common-size service entrances and the generally-accepted, maximum-size motor that each will serve. This assumes the motor is the only other major load supplied by the service entrance.

(Fig. 14). Then the electric range at the house would not prevent adding an electric motor in one of the other buildings. Another advantage is that when installing large motors, you will find it less expensive to use the central distribution arrangement.

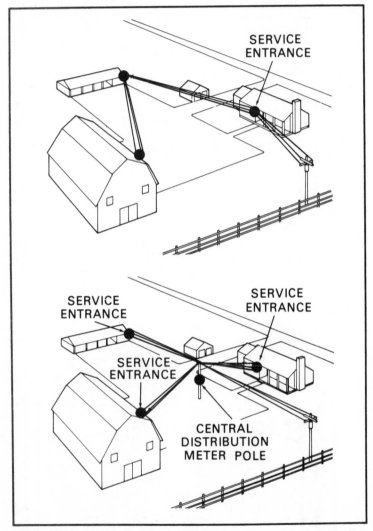

Fig. 14. On many farms, only one service entrance services the home and all service buildings. This is sometimes the case with the small industry. Others have a separate service entrance for each main building, supplied from a central metering pole; this arrangement is better for power equipment.

The central distribution point works equally well if you have a small business with several separate buildings in the same area. Locate the central distribution point nearest the building that will be using the most electric power. This arrangement will give you the least amount of voltage drop—loss of voltage (electrical pressure), which often results when long lengths of wire are used to serve electrical equipment.

B. What Motor Speed (RPM) to Select

Now that you know what power is required of a motor for your equipment, you must determine how fast it should turn. Different pieces of equipment are designed to operate best at specific speeds. Therefore, the motor you select must drive the equipment at the proper speed.

First, you must determine at what speed your equipment should operate. Then, select a motor, or motor and drive, that will best give you that speed. Motor and equipment speeds are measured in terms of revolutions per minute (rpm).

Some fans are equipped with motors that can operate at a number of different speeds. You will find these motors on furnace blowers, attic fans, and portable fans. These motors are usually part of the equipment and only available through large electrical distributors.

There are a few motors available that allow for continuous speed adjustments other than the universal. These motors require special electronic control equipment and must be of the proper type. These motors are sometimes found on fans and drill presses but most often in industrial applications.

There are several sources of information as to the speed of driven equipment. If your equipment is not already equipped with a power unit and you do not know the operating speed, the usual procedure is to get the drive speed from one of the following sources:

- Equipment nameplate (Fig. 3).
- Operator's manual (Fig. 7).
- Local dealer.
- Manufacturer.

If you have equipment that is operating satisfactorily at its present speed, check the speed with a tachometer. A tachometer is an instrument used to measure rotating speed in revolutions per minute (Fig. 15). It shows the revolutions per minute without your having to time the speed over a period of minutes.

If you plan to connect your equipment directly to an electric motor, the operating speeds of each must be the same. It may not always be possible, however, to match the equipment speed with that of a motor. Motors that are most generally available operate at constant no-load speeds of approximately 3600, 1800 and 1200 rpm.

Motors that are designed to operate at a no-load speed of about 1800 rpm are the ones that are in general use. When under load, these motors turn at 1710 to 1750 rpm. An example is the motor on a table saw that is rated to run at a no-load speed of about 1800 rpm when it is not connected to the saw (Fig. 16). When a board is being sawed, the motor is put "under load" and slows to its rated (nameplate) operating speed of 1710 to 1750 rpm.

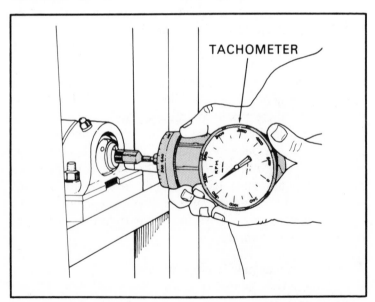

Fig. 15. A tachometer is used to find the speed (rpm) of equipment that is in operation.

Fig. 16. Motors operating with no-load will gradually slow down as the load is applied. For example, this motor operates at about 1800 rpm when not connected to the saw. While sawing, the speed slows to about 1710 to 1750 rpm unless it is overloaded. If overloaded, it will run much slower.

If the equipment to be operated requires a speed different from standard motor speeds, select the motor that has the proper power for your equipment. Then, you will need to use some type of speed-conversion drive system that will give you the proper equipment speed. The drive system may be pulley-and-belt, gear, or chain-and-sprocket. Drive systems are discussed under "III. Selecting Motor Drives."

C. What Motor Duty to Select

After selecting a motor of the correct speed, next you must choose a motor of the proper "duty."

Motor duty refers to the amount of time the motor is operating under full load and how much of the time it is stopped. Manufacturers of motors classify them as follows:

- Continuous duty.
- Intermittent duty.

Most likely, you will find one or the other of these terms on the nameplate (Fig. 3).

Getting a motor for the right duty is important. A motor designed for intermittent duty may not last long when used for continuous duty, because it will overheat. The insulation and wiring are not as good as those in continuous-duty motors, and provisions for air circulation are not as adequate.

Continuous duty is the kind of service in which a motor operates under a constant full load for over 60 minutes at a time. For example, an irrigation pump (Fig. 17), a commercial grinder, and a shredder are continuous operations requiring continuous-duty motors.

Continuous duty is the most common of the two duty classifications for motors used in industry and by commercial concerns. It accounts for about 90 percent of all of their motor applications. If your job calls for continuous operation, you have no choice but to select a continuous-duty motor.

Intermittent duty is the kind of service where the motor operates for alternate periods of load, then no-load; or load

Fig. 17. Example of continuous operation with a continuous-duty motor—motor-driven irrigation pump.

and rest; or load, no-load and rest. Motors for intermittent duty are designed to be fully loaded for periods of 5, 15, 30, or even 60 minutes. Some examples are air compressors (Fig. 18), refrigerators, furnace fans, and pumps on domestic water systems.

The reason for making intermittent-duty motors is a matter of cost. They cost less to build than continuous-duty motors, and this difference in cost is important to a manufacturer who may be using thousands of motors. But, if you only need one or two motors, the difference in cost may not be enough to be important when buying a new motor. Probably the only time you will have to decide whether or not to use an intermittent motor is when you are selecting a used motor.

D. What Motor Type to Select

From the preceding information, you have learned to se-

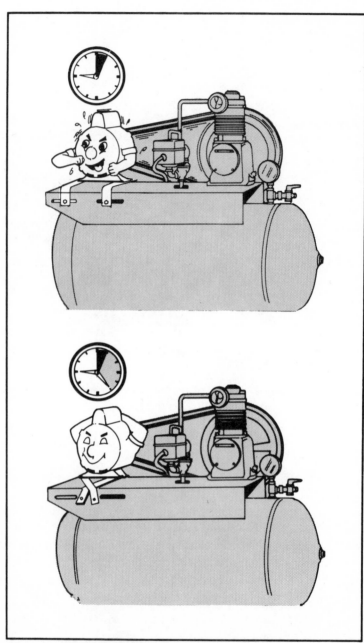

Fig. 18. Example of intermittent operation with an intermittent-duty motor. Motor operates until need is satisfied—from a few seconds to as long as 60 minutes, then motor remains idle for a period of time.

lect the proper size (power), speed (rpm), and duty of the motor to meet your needs. Your next decision is to select the motor type best suited to operate your equipment. To do so, you must know if your equipment is easy or difficult to start. Then select the motor type that can start your load without difficulty.

When you selected the size and speed of the motor needed for your equipment, you used numbers such as ".4 kW (1/2 hp)" and "1800 rpm." Motor types are known by name, such as "capacitor-start" or "repulsion-start, induction-run." Such terms generally describe the design as it relates to the starting mechanism of the motor. Consequently, the names will not mean much to you unless you take time to study the different motor types, their starting characteristics, and their operating principles. Motor types and their starting abilities are discussed here, but motor-operating principles are not.

If a dealer is helping you with the selection of a motor, you do not have too much of a problem. But if you are looking at used motors and trying to get one to fit your needs, it is especially important that you be able to understand about each type of motor.

Figure 19, column 1, lists the various types of motors and, in column 5, you will note that they are all single-phase except the last one. All single-phase motors must have some special provision for starting the motor. These different types have been developed to meet various starting conditions and to keep the first cost as low as possible. This usually means that the motors with the least ability to start a load are also the lowest cost motors.

Three-phase motors need no special starting mechanism. Therefore, any type of 3-phase motor will serve a wide range of jobs. If 3-phase power could be served to all motors, there would be no problem of selecting types, but supplying 3-phase power to all motors, especially those less than .8 kW (1 hp), would be quite costly. Also, in many areas, particularly rural and residential areas, only single-phase power is available. Under these circumstances, there is no choice but to offer various types of motors for single-phase power, even in the larger sizes.

All ac motors rated at .4 kW (1/2 hp) or more have a code

Load Type	Motor Type (1)	Starting Ability (Torque) (2)	Starting Current (3)	Size HP (4)	Phase (5)	Voltage (6)	Speed Range (7)	Reversible (8)	Relative Cost (9)	Other Characteristics (10)	Typical Uses (11)
					Electrical Power Requirements						
Easy Starting Loads	(a) Shaded-Pole Induction	Very low. ½ to 1 times running torque.	Low.	.035–2 kW (1/20–¼ hp)	Single	Usually 120	900 1200 1800 3600	No	Very Low	Light duty, low in efficiency.	Small fans, freezer blowers, arc welder blower, hair dryers.
	(b) Split-Phase	Low. 1 to 1½ times running torque.	High. 6 to 8 times running current.	.035–.56 kW (1/20–¾ hp)	Single	Usually 120	900 1200 1800 3600	Yes	Low	Simple construction.	Fans, furnace blowers, lathes, small shop tools, jet pumps.
	(c) Permanent-Split, Capacitor-Induction	Very low. ½ to 1 times running torque.	Low.	.035–.8 kW (1/20–1 hp)	Single	Single voltage 120 or 240	Variable 900–1800	Yes	Low	Usually custom-designed for special application.	Small Compressors, fans.
	(d) Soft-Start	Very low. ½ to 1 times running torque.	Low. 2 to 2½ times running current.	5.6–25 kW (7½–50 hp)	Single	240	1800 3600	Yes	High	Used in motor sizes normally served by 3-phase power when 3-phase power not available.	Centrifugal pumps, crop dryer fans, feed grinder.

	Type	Starting Torque	Starting Current	kW (hp)	Phase	Voltage	Speed (rpm)	Reversible	Cost/Efficiency	Characteristics	Typical Uses
Difficult Starting Loads	(e) Capacitor-Start, Induction-Run	High. 3 to 4 times running torque.	Moderate. 3 to 6 times running current.	.14–8 kW (1/6–10 hp)	Single	120–240	900 1200 1800 3600	Yes	Moderate	Long service, low maintenance, very popular.	Water systems, air compressors, ventilating fans, grinders, blowers.
	(f) Repulsion-Start, Induction-Run	High. 4 times running torque	Low. 2½ to 3 times running current.	.14–16 kW (1/6–20 hp)	Single	120–240	1200 1800 3600	Yes	Moderate to High	Handles large load variations with little variation in current demand.	Grinders, deep-well pumps, silo unloaders, grain conveyors, barn cleaners.
	(g) Capacitor-Start, Capacitor-Run	High. 3½ to 4½ times running torque.	Medium. 3 to 5 times running current.	.4–20 kW (1/2–25 hp)	Single	120–240	900 1200 1800 3600	Yes	Moderate	Good starting ability and full-load efficiency.	Pumps, air compressors, drying fans, large conveyors, feed mills.
	(h) Repulsion-Start, Capacitor-Run	High. 4 times running torque.	Low. 2½ to 3 times running current.	.8–12 kW (1–15 hp)	Single	Usually 240	1200 1800 3600	Yes	Moderate to High	High efficiency, requires more service than most motors.	Conveyors, deep-well pump, feed mill, silo unloader.
	(i) Three-Phase, General-Purpose	Medium. 2 to 3 times running torque.	High. 3 to 6 times running current.	.4–300 kW (1/2–400 hp)	Three	120–240 240–480 or higher	900 1200 1800 3600	Yes	Very Low	Very simple construction, dependable, service-free.	Conveyors, dryers, elevators, hoists, irrigation pumps.

Fig. 19. Motor Information Chart.

letter on the nameplate. It gives an indication of the current required to start the motor under full load. You will find a list of code letters with the kilovolt-amperes per horsepower in the National Electrical Code.

For example, from the nameplate of an ac motor, you find 1.6 kW (2 hp), 230 volt, 12 amp and code letter M.

From the National Electrical Code, a motor with code letter M requires from 10.0 to 11.19 kilovolt-amperes per horsepower. To find the starting current, multiply the code letter value by 1000 times the horsepower and divide by the voltage. Using a code value of 10.6,

$$\frac{10.6 \times 1000 \times 2\,\text{hp}}{230\,\text{V}} = 92.2 \text{ amperes}$$

Note that this is a little more than 7 times the full load running current.

From your study of this section you will be able to name the motor types and to describe the different starting and operating features of each. You will also learn to list different pieces of equipment according to their starting loads and operating conditions (Fig. 19). With this information about motors and equipment, you can then select the proper motor type for your equipment.

The information you need in order to choose a type of motor is listed under two headings:

   1. Effect of Starting Load and Starting Current on Motor Selected.
   2. Other Factors Affecting the Type of Motor Selected.

1. EFFECT OF STARTING LOAD AND STARTING CURRENT ON MOTOR SELECTED

Motor-driven equipment, unlike gasoline engines, is seldom equipped with a clutch. The motor does not have a chance to develop speed and torque (turning action) before the equipment is engaged. As a result, the motor you select must have sufficient starting torque to start itself and the equipment to which it is connected.

Different types of equipment require different amounts of torque for starting. For example, a fan, a tool grinder, or a bench saw are easy to start, because they are not under full load when they start. Also, there is very little mechanism to start, so there is very little load on the motor.

A meat grinder, piston-type pump, or machine tool offers more resistance to being started. Possibly two or three times more power is needed for starting than for running.

Conveyors or compressors offer still more opposition to being started—perhaps four times as much. Machine tools are not usually loaded when starting, but the mechanism is heavy and it requires a lot of torque to get it started.

Different types of motors also require different amounts of current for starting (Fig. 19, column 3). It is not uncommon for the lights to flicker when motors start. This is because the motor is taking more current for starting than the circuit can supply for the lights and the motor without lowering the voltage. For this reason, you may want to select a motor that has a low starting current. Figure 19A shows schematics of wiring for the different types of motors.

The most important difference in types of motors, however, is in their ability to start a load. For your convenience, the various motor types are grouped into two kinds of starting loads:

    a. Easy Starting Loads.
    b. Difficult Starting Loads.

a. Easy Starting Loads

There are four types of motors designed for easy starting loads (Figs. 19 and 20). They are as follows:

    (1) Shaded-Pole Induction.
    (2) Split-Phase.
    (3) Permanent-Split, Capacitor-Induction.
    (4) Soft-Start.

    (1) SHADED-POLE INDUCTION. The shaded-

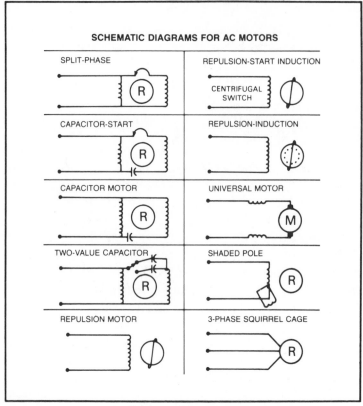

SCHEMATIC DIAGRAMS FOR AC MOTORS

SPLIT-PHASE

REPULSION-START INDUCTION

CENTRIFUGAL SWITCH

CAPACITOR-START

REPULSION-INDUCTION

CAPACITOR MOTOR

UNIVERSAL MOTOR

TWO-VALUE CAPACITOR

SHADED POLE

REPULSION MOTOR

3-PHASE SQUIRREL CAGE

Fig. 19A. Schematics for different types of motors.

pole-induction motor (Figs. 19 and 20) will operate loads that are very easy to start. It has a low starting torque of from 50 to 75 percent of the normal full-speed torque. This type motor may operate on intermittent duty only.

You will note the word "induction" is included in the name of this motor. It could be a part of the name of all of those discussed here, because they are all of the induction type. It is important that you understand that with an induction motor there is no actual electrical connection between the current that feeds to the field coils (stator) and the rotating portion called the rotor (Fig. 21). The electrical currents set up within the rotor are a result of the alternating current in the field coils changing direction 60 times per second. The magnetic effect of this action on the rotor causes it to set up its own voltage and current, without any direct connection to the power supply. This action is called induction.

(2) SPLIT-PHASE. The split-phase motor (Figs. 19 and 20) is satisfactory for small loads that are easy to start. It has a low starting torque of 100 to 150 percent of the normal full-speed torque, and it gives excellent service when used properly.

A split-phase motor has one disadvantage. It will draw from 6 to 8 times its normal running current when starting. This may result in a flicker of lights on that circuit each time it starts.

(3) PERMANENT-SPLIT, CAPACITOR-IN-DUCTION. The permanent-split, capacitor-induction motor may have a capacitor which gives a can-like appearance on the motor (Fig. 22). In some motors the capacitor is located inside the motor housing. This type of capacitor motor has a very low starting torque, 50 to 100 percent of its normal full-speed torque, but it draws a low starting current. It must be used on very easy-to-start loads.

This, and several other motors, have the word "capacitor" in their names. Some electric motors use capacitors to improve the ability of a motor to start a load (Fig. 23). Others use capacitors for both starting and running. How this reaction improves the starting and/or running ability of a motor, however, is beyond the scope of this discussion.

(4) SOFT-START. The soft-start motor (Figs. 19 and 20) was designed originally for agricultural applications. It has a very low starting torque of 50 to 100 percent of the normal full-speed torque. An advantage is that it requires a very low starting current of 2 to 2 1/4 times its normal running current (Fig. 19).

Soft-start motors were developed for users who needed larger motors and who did not have 3-phase power available. Where power suppliers often limit the size motor allowed on a single-phase line to about 4 to 5.6 kW (5 to 7 1/2 hp), they will often allow much larger motors of this type.

b. Difficult Starting Loads

There are six types of motors designed for difficult start-

SHADED-POLE INDUCTION

PERMANENT-SPLIT, CAPACITOR-INDUCTION

Fig. 20. Motors designed for easy starting loads.

ing loads (Fig. 24). They are as follows:

    (1) Capacitor-Start, Induction-Run.
    (2) Repulsion-Start, Induction-Run.
    (3) Capacitor-Start, Capacitor-Run.
    (4) Three-Phase, General-Purpose.
    (5) Perkey Concept.
    (6) Repulsion-Start, Capacitor-Run.

SPLIT-PHASE

SOFT-START

(1) CAPACITOR-START, INDUCTION-RUN. The capacitor-start, induction-run motor (Figs. 19 and 24) is designed to operate difficult starting loads. It will develop about three times more starting torque than the same size split-phase type. The essential difference between this motor and the split-phase motor is the addition of the capacitor along with other design features.

Compared with some electric motors, the capacitor-start,

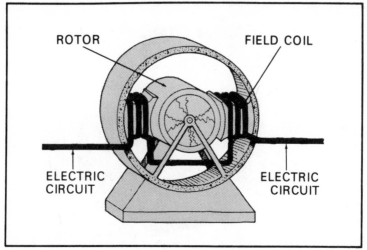

Fig. 21. Induction motors have power supplied to the field coils directly from an electric circuit. There is no direct electrical connection to the rotor. Voltage and current are induced into it.

induction-run motor has a disadvantage. When starting, it draws from 3 to 6 times is full-load running current; therefore, as with the split-phase motor, lights on the same circuit will flicker.

(2) REPULSION-START, INDUCTION-RUN. The repulsion-start, induction-run motor (Figs. 19 and 24) has a high starting torque of 4 times its normal running torque. This type motor is seldom used because the initial cost is higher than the capacitor-start, capacitor-run, and will do the same job.

(3) CAPACITOR-START, CAPACITOR-RUN. The capacitor-start, capacitor-run motor—known also as a "two-value capacitor motor"—(Figs. 19 and 24) also operates on single-phase power. Its starting torque is 3 1/2 to 4 1/2 times the normal running torque. It is different from other capacitor motors in that is has capacitors for both starting and running.

For starting, the capacitor-start, capacitor-run motor requires a fairly heavy current—about 3 to 5 times its normal running current. Some improvements have been made in this respect in more recent models.

CAPACITOR ON TOP

CAPACITOR ON SIDE

Fig. 22. Motors designed with external capacitors. The capacitors may be located on top of motor or on the side of the motor.

(4) THREE-PHASE, GENERAL-PURPOSE. The three-phase, general-purpose motor (Figs. 19 and 24) is adequate for difficult starting loads. It will handle loads that require a starting torque of 2 to 3 times the normal running torque. This is adequate for most hard-to-start jobs. The three-phase, general-purpose motor requires a starting current of 3 to 4 times the normal running current.

A high-starting-torque, three-phase motor is available for extremely difficult starting conditions, but it costs more than the general-purpose type.

Ac poly-phase motors are designed for variable starting torques and load. They also have the highest efficiency, but are generally available in sizes of 15 horsepower or more.

If you have found it difficult to visualize the difference

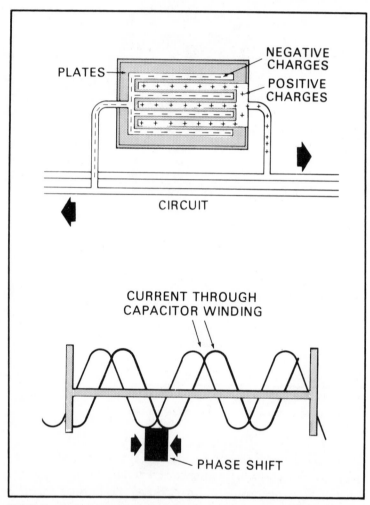

NEGATIVE
CHARGES

PLATES

POSITIVE
CHARGES

CIRCUIT

CURRENT THROUGH
CAPACITOR WINDING

PHASE SHIFT

Fig. 23. In a capacitor, as the alternating current moves in one direction, positive charges build up on one set of plates and negative charges on the other set of plates. As the current changes and starts to flow in the opposite direction, the negative charges flow out or discharge until the plates become neutral. Capacitors are often used in motors to provide for greater starting torque. A phase shift is established between the current flowing in the winding that contains the capacitor and the winding with no capacitor. This shift allows the motor to develop greater starting torque.

between starting and running abilities of motors, see Fig. 25. It shows three of the more common types.

(5) PERKEY CONCEPT. A new method for starting large single-phase and three-phase motors, the Perkey Concept, was introduced in 1980. Under this method, the electric motor is brought up to operating speed by a tractor or diesel engine before the motor is connected to the electrical supply (Figs. 25A and B). This significantly reduces the surge current required for starting the motor. Much larger motors can operate on remote rural lines when their starting surge is reduced. Single-phase motors up to 186 kW (250 hp) are being used on irrigation systems where diesel engines were previously required.

(6) REPULSION-START, CAPACITOR-RUN (Fig. 24). Repulsion-start, capacitor-run motors have a high starting torque. They are used on conveyors, deep-well pumps, feed mills, and silo unloaders. They have a low starting current of 2 to 3 times running current.

2. OTHER FACTORS AFFECTING THE TYPE OF MOTOR SELECTED

Figure 19 shows a number of other factors you may wish to consider in selecting your motor. Some of them are advantages or limitations which you inherit when you select that particular motor type. The more important of these factors are as follows:

   a. Direction of Rotation.
   b. Costs.
   c. Maintenance.

a. Direction of Rotation

Most motors can be wired or adjusted to run in either direction (Fig. 26). Before you purchase a motor, you should know what direction it should turn. Check the rotation of your equipment, then get a motor that will turn in that direction. Figure 19, column 8, shows which types can be reversed. Some

CAPACITOR START, INDUCTION-RUN

CAPACITOR-START, CAPACITOR-RUN

Fig. 24. Motors designed for difficult starting loads.

motors may be reversed with a switch. Repulsion-start motors cannot, however, since the brush position must be changed.

b. Costs

Cost is an important factor. Three-phase motors are usually less expensive than single-phase motors in the larger sizes of .8 kW (1 hp) and up. Sometimes a purchaser will buy a 3-phase motor of the right horsepower, only to find he has

**REPULSION-START,
INDUCTION-RUN**

**THREE-PHASE,
GENERAL-PURPOSE**

a single-phase service. The chart in Fig. 19 (column 9) gives relative costs. For more details as to costs, check with your local dealer.

c. Maintenance

Several types of motors use brushes and a commutator; these are series, repulsion start-induction-run, and repulsion start-capacitor run. These motors have several disadvantages

Fig. 25. Comparison of three common types of single-phase motors as to their ability to start a load. A split-phase motor will start about 1 1/2 times as much load as it will run after it reaches full speed. A capacitor-start motor will start about 3 times as much load as it will run after it reaches full speed. A repulsion-start motor will start about 4 times as much load as it will run after it reaches full speed. All types of motors will deliver their regular rated power after reaching full speed.

not associated with other motors. The brushes cause radio frequency interference due to the arcing between the brushes and commutator. Repulsion-start motors only do this on starting. Due to brush wear, these motors may require more frequent maintenance.

E. What Type of Bearings to Select

You have learned from the previous discussions how to select a motor of the proper size, speed, and duty. You are also able to select the type motor that best suits your needs. Since motors can be supplied with any one of several different

Fig. 25A. Installation of a large electric motor with provisions for bringing it up to operating speed with a farm tractor.

41

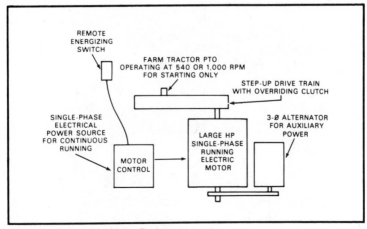

Fig. 25B. Schematic of the Perkey concept.

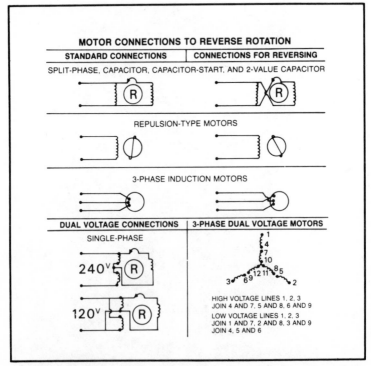

Fig. 26. If a motor is reversible, instructions for reversing the rotation may be found on the back of the panel that covers the electrical connections. For dc motors, reverse either the armature or field connections. For ac single-phase motors, reverse the starting winding connections. For 3-phase motors, interchange any two line loads.

types of bearings, you are now faced with the problem of deciding what type of bearings to get for your motor.

The method and frequency of lubrication will influence your selection. If you get the wrong type of bearings for your needs, they may not last long. Such is the case, if the bearings you get require frequent servicing but your motor is located where it is hard to service. You may tend to neglect servicing. The mounting position of your motor will also affect the type of bearings you use.

The two main types of bearings used on motors are as follows (Fig. 27):

- Sleeve bearings.
- Ball bearings.

The *sleeve-type bearing* is a brass, bronze or tin-lined cylinder in which the shaft rotates (Fig. 27). It provides a smooth, long-wearing surface as long as it is kept well lubricated.

Ball bearings are made up of round steel balls that surround the shaft in a special cage (Fig. 27). As the shaft rotates, the balls roll in their cage. Less friction is created this way.

Before you can decide which type of bearings to select, you must consider the advantages and disadvantages of each. These are discussed under the following headings:

1. Effect of Method and Frequency of Lubrication.
2. Effect of Motor Mounting Position.

1. EFFECT OF METHOD AND FREQUENCY OF LUBRICATION

The method and frequency of lubricating sleeve bearings and ball bearings may determine which bearings best fit your needs. They are given as follows:

a. How Sleeve Bearings Are Lubricated.
b. How Ball Bearings Are Lubricated.

a. How Sleeve Bearings Are Lubricated

Sleeve bearings are lubricated by SAE 20 nondetergent

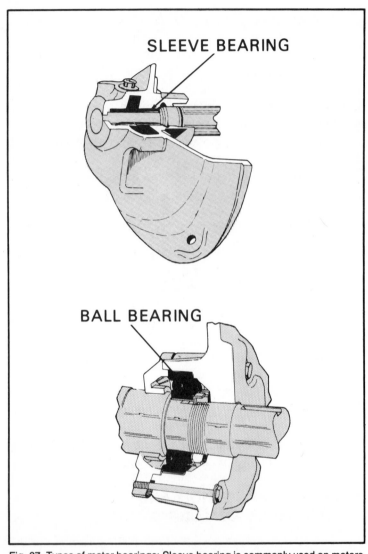

Fig. 27. Types of motor bearings: Sleeve bearing is commonly used on motors of less than .8 kW (1 hp). Ball bearings are commonly used on motors of .8 kW (1 hp) and larger.

or electric motor oil. Avoid over-oiling and always wipe away excess oil. You will find one of the three following oiling systems:

(1) Oil Wick.

(2) Yarn Packed.
(3) Ring Oiled.

(1) OIL WICK. The oil-wick method of lubrication has a wick that extends down into a small oil well under the sleeve bearing (Fig. 28). The wick presses against the motor shaft and feeds the oil by capillary attraction from the well to the motor shaft. At least twice a year, the oil well should be refilled about two-thirds full of new oil.

(2) YARN PACKED. Another method uses oil-soaked yarn packing around the bearing to which a few drops of oil should be added every few months. The yard absorbs the oil and holds it. As the oil supply around the shaft is used, oil from other portions of the yarn feeds into it. If there is a drain plug at the bottom, accumulated oil should be drained off occasionally (Fig. 29). The yarn should be replaced every year or two.

(3) RING OILED. The third method is the use of an oil ring. Oil which clings to the ring is carried from an oil reservoir below the bearing onto the shaft. The ring is loose and turns with the shaft as the motor runs (Fig. 30). With this type is it necessary to keep the oil level up to the filler plug. Check monthly. Every two or three years it is well to drain

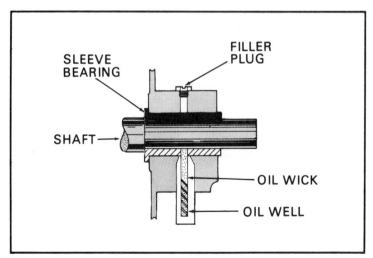

Fig. 28. Some small motors have oil-wick lubricated bearings.

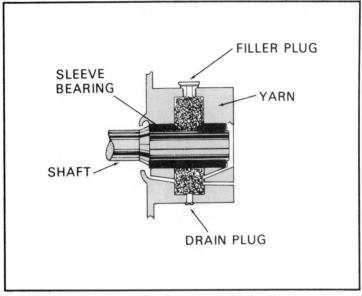

Fig. 29. Many motors have oil-soaked, yarn packed bearings.

the oil, flush out the reservoir with solvent, and add new oil.

b. How Ball Bearings Are Lubricated

Ball bearings do not require as much attention as sleeve bearings. They are lubricated by grease which is recirculated by the bearings in the bearing cavity.

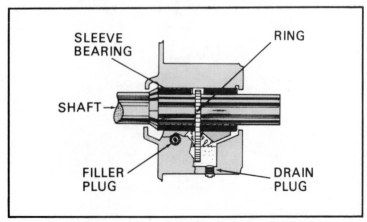

Fig. 30. Larger sleeve-bearing motors often have ring-oiled bearings.

Three methods by which ball bearings are lubricated are:

(1) Prelubricated and sealed at the factory.
(2) Disassembled and hand packed.
(3) Lubricated through special fittings.

(1) PRELUBRICATED AND SEALED. Prelubricated and sealed bearings do not require any additional lubrication. This is the type to use if your motor is not easily accessible.

(2) HAND PACKED. Bearings that are disassembled and hand packed should be lubricated every two to five years.

(3) SPECIAL FITTINGS. Bearings that are lubricated through special fittings (Fig. 31) have both a filler and a drain plug. Lubricate these bearings approximately every two years. Remove bottom plug before greasing. Then operate motor for a few seconds to relieve pressure before replacing plugs to prevent rupturing grease seal. Use multipurpose grease.

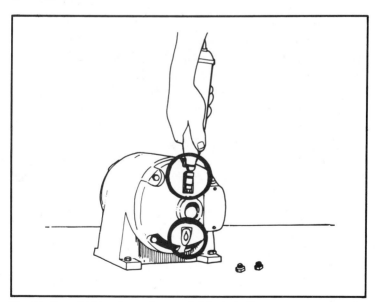

Fig. 31. Some ball-bearing motors are lubricated with a grease gun containing special ball-bearing grease.

2. EFFECT OF MOTOR MOUNTING POSITION

The position in which your motor is to be mounted may be the determining factor in your selection of bearings. The main reason is the difference in the way bearings are lubricated. Second, end thrust and radial load may influence your decision.

Sleeve bearings are lubricated through an opening in the sleeve. Grooves then deliver the oil to all parts of the shaft. An oil-lubricated, sleeve-bearing motor will work fine as long as the shaft is mounted parallel with the floor. Most FHP, sleeve bearing motors have all-position (all-angle) bearings.

Note in Fig. 32 that a sleeve-bearing motor can be mounted in the floor position (Fig. 32), in the wall position (Fig. 32), or in the ceiling position (Fig. 32). If changed from the floor to the wall position, the end shields must be loosened and rotated a quarter turn. This keeps the oil from running out of the oil reservoirs, but it does not affect the operation of the motor. If it is mounted in the ceiling position, the end shields must be rotated one-half turn. With some motors it may not be possible to rotate the end shields that much because of short wire leads inside the motor.

There are special cases where sleeve bearings may be used in a vertical position. One design has spiral grooves on the shaft that act as a pump to carry the oil up the shaft. Another is a special oil-soaked bronze bearing.

Since *ball-bearing* motors are grease lubricated, they can be mounted in any position without loss of lubricant. A drill press is an example of a vertical mounting (Fig. 33). This feature also makes them adaptable to portable equipment.

If the motor shaft must carry much additional end thrust, as in power drills, vertical lawn mowers, and turbine pumps, be sure to get a motor with a special end-thrust ball-bearing (Fig. 33).

Motors designed for vertical mounting have the bearing designed so the outer race extends over the top of the balls for upward thrust and extends under the balls for downward thrust.

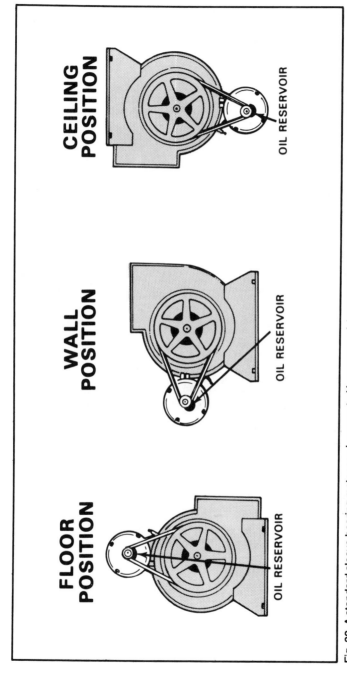

Fig. 32. A standard sleeve-bearing motor can be mounted in any one of three positions: floor, wall, or ceiling. NOTE: Protective shields must be installed before operation.

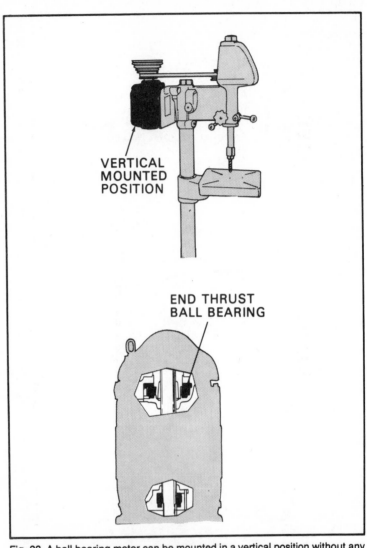

VERTICAL
MOUNTED
POSITION

END THRUST
BALL BEARING

Fig. 33. A ball-bearing motor can be mounted in a vertical position without any lubrication problem.

F. What Type of Enclosure to Select

In addition to other decisions you have made in selecting a motor, you must also select the proper type of *enclosure*, or housing, for your motor. The enclosure refers to the end shields, or the end bells as they are sometimes called, that support the bearing housings and protect both ends of the motor.

If all motors could be totally enclosed, there would be no decision. But motors produce heat while operating which must be removed to keep the motor from getting too hot. The easiest and least expensive method of providing cooling is for the manufacturer to leave openings in both end shields so the built-in fan can circulate air through the motor (Fig. 34).

Your selection of a motor enclosure depends on the environment in which your motor will operate. If your motor is to operate in a clean, dry place, you can use any type of motor enclosure. If there are dirt and moisture conditions that may be harmful to your motor, select a type of enclosure that will protect it. For example, if your motor is to be operated in dusty conditions such as near a feed mill, it must be protected against dust. If not, the dust will collect in the windings and interfere with proper cooling, causing the motor to to overheat.

This discussion is to acquaint you with the different types

Fig. 34. Some motors are fan-cooled by the circulation of outside air through the motor.

of motor enclosures and the conditions for which they are built. From the following information, you will be able to select the proper enclosure for each environment:

1. Types of Motor Enclosures Available.
2. Effect of Water Spray on Motor Enclosure Selected.
3. Effect of Dust on Motor Enclosure Selected.
4. Effect of Other Conditions on Motor Enclosure Selected.

1. TYPES OF MOTOR ENCLOSURES AVAILABLE

Some motors used on home appliances are "open" and are not well protected. For protection, when operating in harmful environments such as dust or moisture, motors are made with three different types of enclosures. They are generally known as follows (Fig. 35):

a. Dripproof.
b. Totally-enclosed.
c. Explosion-proof.

a. Dripproof

The type of enclosure you select helps determine how much cooling air can be moved through the motor. The dripproof type, often called the open-type enclosure (Fig. 35), provides for rather easy movement of air through the end shield into the motor mechanism. This is a highly desirable arrangement if clean air can be provided and free water kept from entering the motor.

b. Totally-enclosed

Totally-enclosed motors provide no openings for circulation of outside air through the motor. Instead, an internal fan circulates only that air which is inside the housing, or an external fan is provided. Because of this, these motors usually run at a higher temperature than the other two types. They also cost more. When totally enclosed, the motor is well pro-

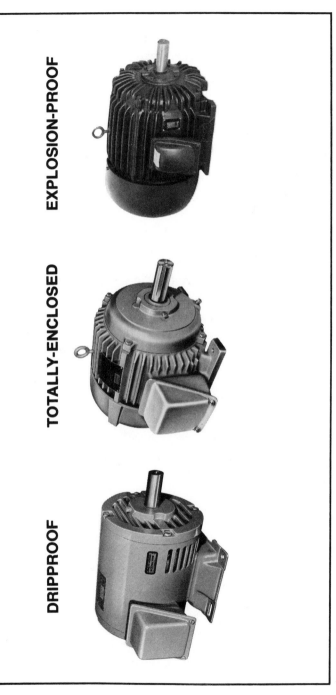

DRIPPROOF   TOTALLY-ENCLOSED   EXPLOSION-PROOF

Fig. 35. Types of motor enclosures.

tected from dirt, moisture, and falling objects.

Because the air circulation is reduced or stopped by the enclosure, the manufacturer has to take into account the fact that the temperatures will rise because of the additional difficulty of getting rid of the heat. This affects the quality of insulation and the way the motor is made. Consequently, the manufacturer indicates on the nameplate the ambient temperature of 40 °C (Fig. 3).

Motors are not only limited for use by the power ratings. There are two other limiting factors: ambient temperatures and class of insulation. Ambient temperature (temperature of the surrounding area when the motor is being operated) will limit the use of the motor. Operating temperatures and classes of insulation in the motor are directly related to the life of the motor. Insulations are rated by alphabetical letters such as A, B, F, and H. The higher alphabet letters designations indicate longer life at higher temperatures.

Manufacturers sometimes overcome the heat problem of the totally-enclosed motor by "beefing up" the horsepower. With a totally-enclosed motor a manufacturer will often use a size larger assembly than that indicated on the rating so as to keep down the heat rise. For example, a 1.1 kW (1 1/2 hp) mechanism might be used in a .8 kW (1 hp) totally-enclosed motor.

In the event that a motor will be subject to direct washdown such as in processing facilities or a dairy, a totally enclosed type enclosure should be used.

c. Explosion Proof

There are two categories of explosion-proof motors: *explosion-proof* and *dust ignition resistant*. So, you see, the term "explosion-proof" may include other motors designed for hazardous locations.

2. EFFECT OF WATER SPRAY ON MOTOR ENCLOSURE SELECTED

If your motor is to be used where water or other noncorrosive liquids are present, you choose between a dripproof

(Fig. 35) or a totally enclosed (Fig. 35) type of enclosure. Your choice will be determined by the condition under which water might enter the motor.

If your motor is to be used where it is exposed to weather or splashing water, you should select a weather protected or totally enclosed motor enclosure (Fig. 35) which has shielded ventilation openings. This type of enclosure protects the motor from falling objects and liquids and also from objects or liquids that strike it from the side, unless they enter at a very low angle.

One type of totally-enclosed motor is the submersible. It is generally cooled by the force of the liquid passing around the housing. Submersible motors are used for pumping water and other liquids (Fig. 35B).

3. EFFECT OF DUST ON MOTOR ENCLOSURE SELECTED

If your motor is to operate in dusty conditions such as around a feed mill or a concrete mixing plant, you may decide

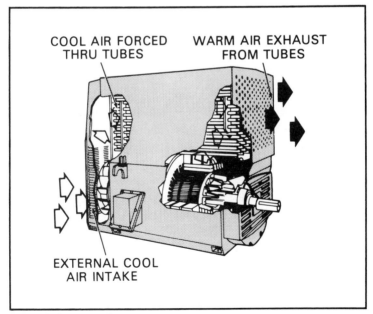

COOL AIR FORCED THRU TUBES

WARM AIR EXHAUST FROM TUBES

EXTERNAL COOL AIR INTAKE

Fig. 35A. An externally-cooled, totally enclosed motor.

Fig. 35B. A submersible motor.

to get an explosion proof motor. It may be possible, however, to locate your motor away from the dust. This is sometimes done by using an extended drive shaft and partitioning off the area in which the motor is located so it is relatively free of dust. Single-phase motors are particularly susceptible to dust. They have mechanical and electrical parts that can easily become clogged with dust and dirt.

Motor manufacturers are developing more efficient motors than in the past (Fig. 35C). Also inverters are being produced to vary the speed of ac motors when the job demands.

Totally-enclosed motors cost 20 and 40 percent more than drip-proof motors but they are not affected by dust. Therefore, the extra cost can often be saved by avoiding repair bills. Use

Fig. 35C. Comparison of two 1 1/2 hp polyphase motors showing improvements for energy efficiency and power factor. The motor on the left has a longer rotor and stator cores that reduce magnetic flux density. There is more copper wire in the stator and aluminum in the rotor to cut resistance and improve conductivity. Air gaps are optimized to reduce current requirements and stray load losses. Special steel processing in the stator helps minimize core losses. Improved winding distribution helps maximize energy use. As a result, the motor runs cooler, uses less energy and lasts longer.

explosion-proof motors where dust is combustible.

4. EFFECT OF OTHER CONDITIONS ON MOTOR ENCLOSURE SELECTED

In addition to water spray and dust, you may have other conditions which will affect your selection of a motor enclosure. They are as follows:

• Exposure to corrosive materials requires motors made of noncorrosive materials.
• Submersion in water or other liquid requires sealed enclosures.
• Presence of explosive gases requires explosion-proof motors.
• Moisture problems during off seasons. Space heating elements are available for motors such as those for irrigation pumps that stand idle.

• Rodents. Screens are available to cover the openings of drip-proof motors to keep out rodents and other creatures.

Check with your local dealer or manufacturer regarding these special conditions.

G. What Type of Mounting Base to Select

The information given here will help you select the proper mounting base for your equipment. The life of your motor may depend partly on the type of base you select. Keeping a motor in proper alignment and free of vibration can help reduce bearing wear.

The purposes of a mounting base are as follows:

• Provide a means for anchoring the motor in position.
• Provide a means for tightening a belt drive.
• Provide alignment of the motor.
• In some cases, reduce vibration on the motor or else reduce motor vibration noise.

The frame type is normally designated on the nameplate of an electric motor. This is a rating established by the National Electrical Manufacturers Association (NEMA) and refers to the particular physical details of the motor that would be of importance in motor replacement. Two motors supplied by different manufacturers but with the same frame number could be interchanged and all mounting holes, shaft size, and keyway would be compatible. Motors manufactured since 1965 have smaller size frames than pre-1965 motors. Your motor base may require some adjustment to accommodate this smaller motor.

There are many types of motor mounts. Two are shown here (Figs. 36 and 37).

Manufacturers equip most fractional-power motors for general use with a pressed steel rigid base attached to the motor. There is usually one slotted hole in each corner of the base (Fig. 36). The slotted holes make it possible to adjust

RIGID BASE
(FIXED TO MOTOR FRAME)

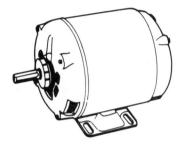

RIGID BASE
(WITH ADJUSTING SCREWS)

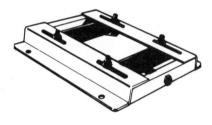

SLIDING RAILS
(WITH ADJUSTING SCREWS)

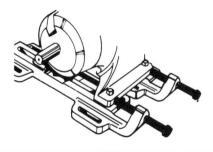

Fig. 36. Types of rigid motor bases.

Fig. 37. Cushion base. Used to keep down motor noise or to protect the motor if it is mounted on equipment that vibrates.

the motor forward and backward to tighten or loosen belts or to align the motor.

If your motor has no adjusting slots, which is usually the case with motor sizes of .8 kW (1 hp) or larger, you will need to supply a sliding base or sliding rails. A sliding base (Fig. 36) or sliding rails (Fig. 36) provide for both alignment and belt adjustment. These bases have one or more adjusting screws so it is easy to move the motor back and forth.

If your motor is mounted on equipment that vibrates, you should use a cushion base (Fig. 37). It provides a rubber cushion support for each end of the motor which dampens vibration that, otherwise, could destroy a motor.

About the only time you are likely to need this type of base is when you are replacing a motor already protected with a cushion-mounted base. If the new motor does not fit the old base, get a new cushioned base for the motor. It costs about five percent more than a rigid base.

Sometimes, if a motor is mounted on a thin sheet-metal

housing such as on a fan housing, the vibration from the motor may be magnified by the sheet metal into a disturbing noise. A cushion-mounted base usually overcomes this noise.

H. What Motor Efficiency to Select

The selection of high-efficiency electric motors represents an energy conservation action for profit—your profit. It is a measure that can be easily taken to reduce often significant energy consumption.

Take time to evaluate the technical characteristics of the motors that are to be purchased. Perform a payback analysis of those that meet the requirements. Determine the savings to be obtained over the life of the motor. Now multiply this savings by the number of motors to be purchased. These are simple but practical steps that should be a part of every energy management program.

Electric motors in the United States consume more energy than automobiles. The proper selection, application, and maintenance of electric motors is essential to energy conservation and should be a part of your energy management program.

Procedures for computing the payback period are as follows:

1. *Determine average energy cost per kWh.*

$$\text{Average (kWh) Cost} = \frac{\text{Total Electric Bill}}{\text{kWh Consumed}}$$

2. *Obtain efficiencies of motors selected.*

$$\text{Efficiency} = \frac{\text{Power Input}}{\text{Power Output}}$$

If the efficiency is not on the motor nameplate, contact the motor supplier.

3. *Calculate kilowatts saved.*

$$\text{Kilowatts Saved} = \text{Horsepower} \times (10^{-3}) \times 736 \times \alpha$$

$$\text{where } \alpha = \frac{1}{\text{(Motor \#1 Efficiency)}} - \frac{1}{\text{(Motor \#2 Efficiency)}}$$

4. *Calculate motor price differential.*

$$\text{Price (\$)} = \text{Motor Cost (1)} - \text{Motor Cost (2)}$$

5. *Calculate economic payback.*

$$\text{Payback (yrs)} = \frac{\text{Motor Premium Price Differential}}{\text{kW saved} \times \text{(avg. kWh cost)} \times \text{motor operation hrs/year}}$$

I. What Motor Power Factor to Select

The power factor of a motor is a measure of how well the motor uses the current it draws. The power factor is expressed in terms of real current and reactive current:

$$\text{Power factor} \quad \frac{\text{Real current}}{\text{Total current}}$$

The reactive current creates the magnetic field within the motor while the real current produces power and does the work. The total current for a motor is the sum of the real and reactive currents.

In general, small motors are often inefficient, having power factors below 70 percent, while power factors are greater in the more efficient, larger hp integral ac-polyphase motors. The average-size polyphase motor sold is about 15 hp, and it is in the 5–20 hp range that inefficiencies often appear.

If the motor nameplate does not specify power factor, contact your motor supplier. If, for example, the power factor is below a certain percent, you may be assessed a "power factor penalty" by the utility company. This can amount to several dollars per month.

Part II

Selecting Motor

Overload Protective Devices

No matter what motor you select as to size, speed, duty, type, bearings, enclosure, or mount, you must provide for starting and stopping the motor. But, more important, you must provide for some type of overload protection. Since overload protection is often included in the control (starter switch), in this section the two are discussed together when that is the situation.

Overload protection for your motor is important to you (Fig. 38), because it is a form of motor insurance. An overloaded condition on a motor will cause it to need more current than it is designed to use. Too much current will cause the windings to overheat. Continued overheating will cause the insulation to break down and the motor will "burn up."

Excessive current will flow to the motor if one, or both, of the following conditions exist:

• *The load is too heavy.* There are several causes for extra-heavy loads. The driven machine may become jammed or locked, a belt-driven machine may have a belt that is too tight, the sheave on the motor may be out of line with the sheave on the equipment, or the bearings may be worn or in need of lubrication.

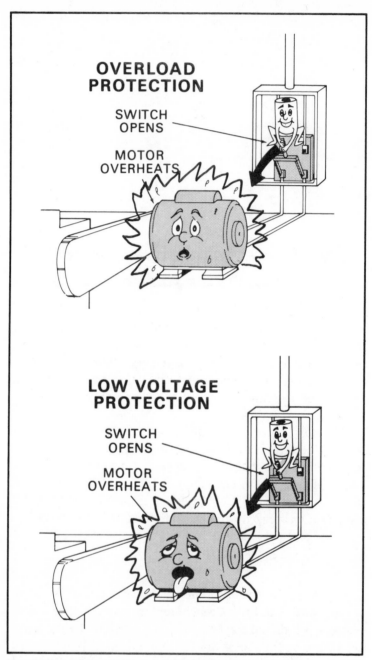

OVERLOAD PROTECTION

SWITCH OPENS

MOTOR OVERHEATS

LOW VOLTAGE PROTECTION

SWITCH OPENS

MOTOR OVERHEATS

Fig. 38. You can get motor controls that will protect against too much load, and protect against low voltage.

• *The voltage is too low.* Low voltage is usually caused by the feeder wires from the service entrance to the motor being too small. Or, the power supplier may have trouble providing proper voltage. The latter is usually a temporary situation which the power supplier can correct if told of the trouble.

You cannot always tell when these conditions may exist. You need help. You get this help by selecting the right type of overload protective device for your motor. Study the factors that follow.

A. What Motor Overload Protection to Use

You should keep in mind that the fuse, which protects the wiring circuit, does not protect your motor from overload or low voltage. It is there to protect the circuit wires only. Therefore, other protective measures are necessary.

From this discussion you will be able to name and identify the different types of controls and overload protective devices, and to describe the principles on which they work. You will also learn how to select the proper types of protective devices for different sizes of motors and for different motor uses.

This information is given under the following headings:

1. Types of Overload Protective Devices and How They Work.
2. Effect of Motor Size on Protective Device Selected.
3. Effect of the Type of Operation on Protective Device Selected.
4. Effect of Power Supplier's Requirements on Protective Device Selected.

1. TYPES OF OVERLOAD PROTECTIVE DEVICES AND HOW THEY WORK

In studying each of the overload control principles, you will see that with each one something must be heated before the overload switch opens. This gives a time-delay action, which is important during starting. Here is the reason. A motor takes more current to start than it does to run after it gets started—this is especially true on hard-to-start loads. That means that the overload control must be designed to allow enough time for the motor to start without opening the circuit.

Also, a motor can stand an overload for a short time and not be damaged. To meet this condition, the overload control is selected so it will provide for at least 15 percent temporary overload but not more than 25 percent overload. If the overload continues to be greater than 25 percent, the control will open the circuit.

From the standpoint of a user, the different types of motor controls and protective devices are as follows:

a. Built-In Overload Protection in the Motor.
b. Manual Starting Switch with Overload Protection.
c. Magnetic Starting Switch with Overloaded Protection.
d. Time-Delay Fuse in Motor Disconnect Switch.
e. Current-Limiting Starter.

a. Built-In Overload Protection in the Motor.

This type of protective device is mounted in the motor by the manufacturer. There are two types of built-in protectors (Fig. 39):

(1) Manual-Reset Type.
(2) Automatic-Reset Type.

Both types operate on the heat (thermal-overload of bimetallic strip) principle (Fig. 40).

(1) MANUAL-RESET TYPE. Manual-reset means that you must press a button to reset the tripped mechanism before the motor will start again. With most uses it is better for you to have to reset the tripped mechanism. This gives you a chance to check for the cause of the overload. It also cuts out any chance of your getting caught in the equipment

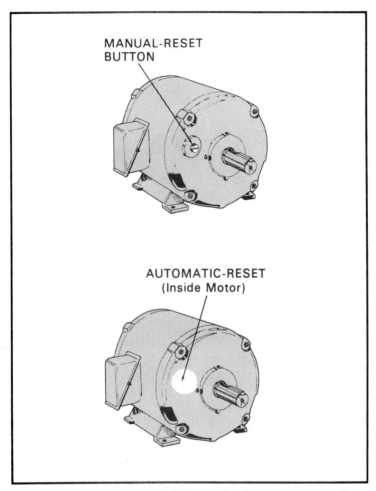

MANUAL-RESET
BUTTON

AUTOMATIC-RESET
(Inside Motor)

Fig. 39. Types of overload control. With the manual-reset type, motor will not start after being overloaded until the user pushes the button to reset the control. The automatic type starts the motor automatically after it has cooled.

while you are checking it, because the motor will not start until you press the control reset button.

(2) AUTOMATIC-RESET TYPE. The automatic-reset type works as shown in Fig. 41. It recloses without your aid. When the heater in the control cools, the bimetallic disk snaps into the opposite position (Fig. 41). The contacts close and the motor restarts (or tries to restart if overloaded).

With either type of built-in protection the motor may be

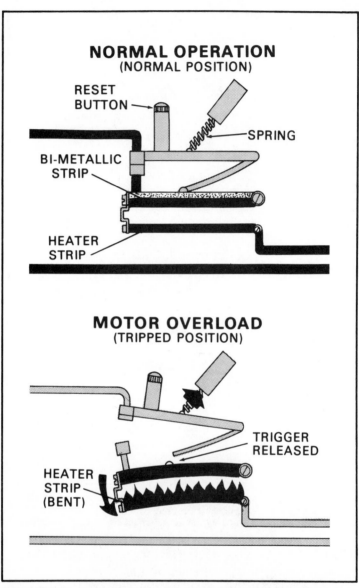

Fig. 40. How a manual-reset, bimetallic overload control works. Electrons (current) move through the heated strip when operating within its rated capacity. With an overload, the heater strip becomes hot. The heat, being so close to the bimetallic strip, causes it to heat and bend. When heated sufficiently, the bimetallic strip bends enough to release the trigger. The spring pulls the electrical contacts apart, thus opening the circuit. After the bimetallic strip has cooled, it straightens to its original position. Then, you can press the reset button and reset the switch which turns the current back on.

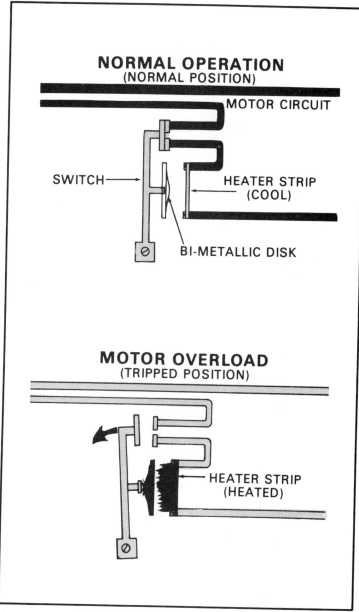

Fig. 41. An automatic-reset type of built-in protector. When overload occurs, the heater strip heats the bimetallic disk. When heated, the disk snaps to the left, "tripping" the switch and opening the circuit. When the heater strip cools, the disk snaps back to its original position. The circuit is closed and the motor restarts automatically.

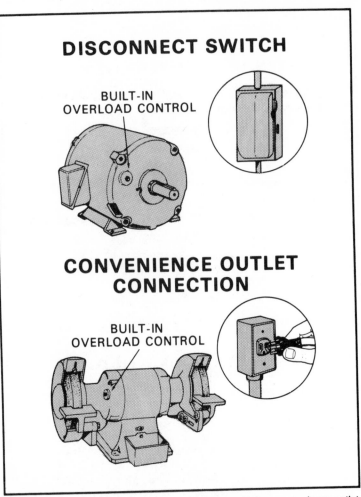

DISCONNECT SWITCH

BUILT-IN
OVERLOAD CONTROL

CONVENIENCE OUTLET
CONNECTION

BUILT-IN
OVERLOAD CONTROL

Fig. 42. Motors with built-in protection may be plugged into a convenience outlet or connected to a disconnect switch.

plugged in directly (Fig. 42) or connected to a disconnect switch (Fig. 42).

b. Manual Starting Switch with Overload Protection

The overload control in this kind of switch will work either on the principle shown in Fig. 40, or on that in Fig. 43. Either one must be equipped with a heater strip (or heater

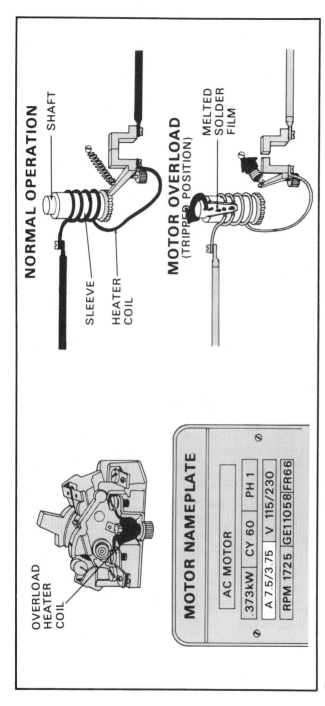

NORMAL OPERATION

SHAFT

SLEEVE

HEATER COIL

MOTOR OVERLOAD
(TRIPPED POSITION)

MELTED SOLDER FILM

OVERLOAD HEATER COIL

MOTOR NAMEPLATE

AC MOTOR		
373kW	CY 60	PH 1
A 7.5/3.75	V 115/230	
RPM 1725	GE11058	FR66

Fig. 43. A manually-operated switch was a built-in, solder-and-ratchet type of control. Note how the heater coil fits over the sleeve and how the shaft and ratchet wheel are fastened together. The shaft is held in place in the sleeve with solder during normal motor operation. Continued overload melts the solder, allowing spring to rotate the shaft and ratchet wheel, thus opening motor circuit. When solder cools, it hardens and holds shaft in place. Control is then reset by hand.

73

coil) with a rating that either matches the amperage on your motor nameplate or is not more than 25 percent greater (Fig. 43). For totally-enclosed motors, the limit is 15 percent. There is a wide selection of heater strips for each make of switch, so this is no problem. The important thing is for you, or your dealer, to see that the right one is installed in the control at the time you buy it.

A manually-operated switch with the built-in overload control, and used with .4 to 2.5 kW (1/2 to 3 hp) motors, is shown in Fig. 43. The heater coil shown is for 120-volt operation. If used on 240-volt service, the heater coil would be three to five amperes. Some heater coils are numbered with only catalog numbers. To get their amperage rating, it is necessary to check the manufacturer's catalog.

c. Magnetic Starting Switch with Overload Protection

This type of control has overload protection built into the switch which gives the same protection as the manual type. The difference in the two switches' protection is in the way the motor is started. Instead of a manual switch to open and close the circuit, this switch works with a manual or automatic control and a magnetic switch. Here is how the magnetic switch and overload control work.

To operate a magnetic switch which, in turn, starts the motor, you press on the start push button A (Fig. 44). This completes the circuit that energizes the solenoid (magnetic) switch. Current flows from the supply line B, through the push-button switch C, through the switch you are pressing A, through the solenoid coil D, through the overload control switch E, and back to the other supply line F. This completes the circuit that energizes the solenoid.

With the solenoid energized (Fig. 44), the solenoid shaft is pulled upwards by magnetic attraction. This causes all three sets of contacts attached to the shaft to close. The two lower sets of contacts complete the circuit to the motor, causing it to start. The upper contacts provide a new circuit for keeping the solenoid energized without your having to hold the

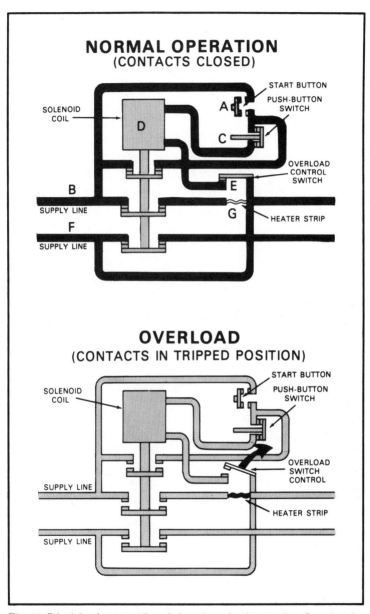

Fig. 44. Principle of a magnetic switch and overload protection. Pressing the start button energizes the solenoid circuit and activates the solenoid. With solenoid energized, switch contacts are closed to start the motor. The solenoid remains energized by a special circuit that bypasses the start button. The heater strip protects the motor from overload by causing the bimetallic switch to open when current flow is great enough to cause excess heat.

starter button down. The solenoid continues to hold all contacts closed until the solenoid circuit is opened.

Overload protection is provided in much the same manner as with the other controls. As current flows through the motor circuit, it passes through heater strip G (Fig. 44). Heat is given off, but not enough to cause the bimetallic overload control switch to open unless there is continuing overload on the motor. When the motor is overloaded, the flow of current through the heater strip increases enough to develop extra heat. This causes the bimetallic strip to open the switch and open the solenoid circuit. The solenoid loses magnetism, which releases the solenoid shaft. All three sets of contacts open. The motor stops and will not start again until the overload control is reset and the start button pressed again.

When you wish to stop the motor, pressing the stop button also opens the solenoid circuit in the same manner as when the overload switch opened the circuit.

An example of this type of switch is shown in Fig. 45.

If there is extremely low voltage on the power supply line or if power is off momentarily, the solenoid will lose its

Fig. 45. A remote, push-button control used with a magnetic switch.

magnetic effect. That is why these switches are said to provide protection against low voltage or no voltage.

If a magnetic switch is used for 3-phase motors, the action is the same except there is a fourth set of contacts on the solenoid shaft to take care of the third line feeding from the power supply to the motor circuit.

d. Time-Delay Fuse in Motor Disconnect Switch

The time-delay fuse (sometimes called a dual element or a delayed-action fuse) takes care of temporary overloads which cause a motor to use more than a normal amount of current. This is often the condition when a motor starts equipment that is already connected to it or when the unit it is driving is suddenly overloaded. Under these conditions, a standard fuse will blow as soon as the current flow becomes greater than the amperage rating marked on it.

Figure 46 shows how a time-delay fuse works. Note that it has a fuse link the same as all regular fuses, except current at which fuse "blows" is higher for the given amperage rating. Additions are the spring and solder cup which provide the delayed action. When current flow increases to more than the rating indicated on the fuse, the coil around the solder cup gradually heats the solder and softens it. If the heating action continues, the solder will soften enough for the spring to pull the fuse link out of the solder. When that happens, the circuit is opened. The fuse will have to be replaced before the motor can be started again.

In case of a short circuit, the fuse link blows before the solder cup has time to heat.

Time-delay fuses are available in two types: (1) plug fuse (Fig. 47) and (2) cartridge fuse (Fig. 47).

There are two kinds of time-delay plug fuses. One fits any standard plug fuse socket (Fig. 47). It has the disadvantage that when the fuse blows, it can be replaced with a standard plug fuse of any size, or with another size of time-delay fuse. If you do not have the right size to replace the blown one, you may be tempted to substitute with another that is of higher amperage. This could mean that your wiring has little or no protection.

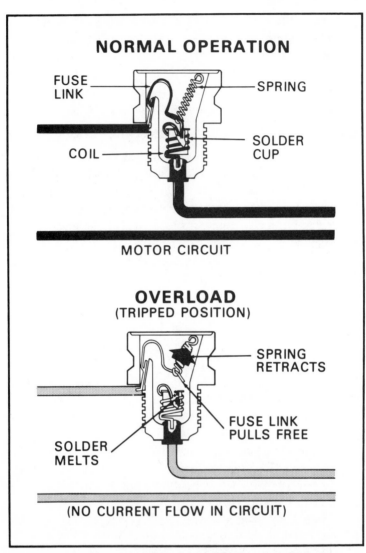

NORMAL OPERATION

FUSE LINK

SPRING

COIL

SOLDER CUP

MOTOR CIRCUIT

OVERLOAD
(TRIPPED POSITION)

SPRING RETRACTS

FUSE LINK PULLS FREE

SOLDER MELTS

(NO CURRENT FLOW IN CIRCUIT)

Fig. 46. Time-delay fuse. Overheating works on same principle as in Figs. 40 and 43. Under overload conditions, excess current melts solder in solder cup, allowing spring to pull fuse link from cup, thus opening the circuit. The old fuse must be replaced with a new one of the same size.

The second kind of time-delay plug fuse is made with a special adapter called a "Type S fuse" (Fig. 47). This is to prevent the possibility of substituting with fuses of the wrong size. The adapter fits any standard plug-fuse socket, and, because of its design, once the adapter is screwed into the socket, it cannot be removed. Although a particular adapter can be used with several different (amperage) sizes, the range of sizes that can be used is so small no serious error can be made.

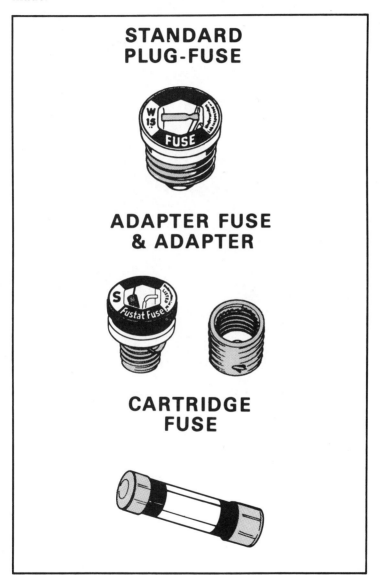

Fig. 47. Types of time-delay fuses.

Fig. 48. Reduced voltage starter.

If your motor is protected with cartridge fuses, there are cartridge time-delay fuses that protect the motor in the same way as the plug-type (Fig. 47).

e. Current-Limiting Starters

Various types of current-limiting devices are used as starting equipment for the larger electric motors. The current-limiting starters are often required by power suppliers, especially on 5.6 kW (7 1/2 hp) and larger single-phase motors.

Most of the starters discussed here (across-the-line

starters) operate by closing the circuit to the motor. When the circuit is closed, the motor takes all the current it needs to get started. An across-the-line starter, combined with 5.6 kW (7 1/2 hp) motors or larger, often cause your lights to dim and possibly your neighbor's. This can cause a bad line condition for the power supplier for a distance of several miles unless the power line has ample reserve capacity or unless you are located close to the substation or power source.

2. EFFECT OF MOTOR SIZE ON PROTECTIVE DEVICE SELECTED

Always check the National Electrical Code requirements for controls and protective devices. For example, safety switches for motors of over 1500 W (2 hp) require a nameplate rating in watts or horsepower. The size of your motor is the main factor in deciding which type of control and overload protection to get. The following table gives the types that are suitable for different size motors:

Size of Motor (Horsepower)	Type of Control and Overload Protection
0–⅓	Built-in overload protection with manual reset (Figure 39).
½–2	Built-in overload protection with manual reset (Figure 39).
½–3	Manual starting switch with overload protection (Figure 43).
5 or larger	Magnetic starting switch with overload protection (Figure 44).
Any size	Time-delay fuse in motor disconnect switch (Figure 46).
7½ or larger (single phase only)	Current-limiting (resistor) starter (sometimes required by power supplier), manual starting switch with overload protection (Figure 48).

3. EFFECT OF THE TYPE OF OPERATION ON PROTECTIVE DEVICE SELECTED

You may have one of three different types of operations which will influence your selection of a protective device. The National Electric Code governs sizes of motor-protection devices. Always refer to the Code when selecting controls and protective devices. They are as follows:

    a. Manually Controlled.
    b. Remote Controlled.
    c. Unattended.
    d. Three-Phase.

a. Manually Controlled

If your motor is to be manually controlled, you can use any type of protective device. If your motor is .4 to 2.5 kW (1/2 to 3 hp), the manual starting switch with overload protection is the least expensive. For example, the time-delay fuse is low in cost and will provide good protection for almost any type of operation, and you can buy it in amperage sizes to fit most size motors. Fuse sizes may range from approximately the same amperage as shown on the motor nameplate to 25 percent greater to provide proper protection.

b. Remote Controlled

If your motor is to be controlled by a remote control switch (Fig. 45), use a magnetic starting switch with overload protection. The remote control should have a manual reset button in the control box. The magnetic starting switch is used mostly with 4 kW (5 hp) motors and larger. The cost of the starter keeps it from being used much for smaller motors.

c. Unattended

If your motor is to operate unattended such as on an air conditioner, a water pump, or a crop drier, the automatic-reset type could be used. This feature is generally available in two types of protective devices: built-in overload protection and manual starting switch with automatic reset.

According to the National Electric Code, you are not allowed to install an automatic reset if there is a hazard created by the automatic restarting of the motor and equipment.

d. Three-Phase

Remember, if you have a three-phase motor, it has three power leads. Each one of the three leads must be protected.

4. EFFECT OF POWER SUPPLIER'S REQUIREMENTS ON PROTECTIVE DEVICE SELECTED

If you have a 5.6 kW (7 1/2 hp) or larger motor that is to operate on single-phase power, you may be required by your power supplier to get a current-limiting type starter. This type of starter helps prevent the lights from dimming in the surrounding area when the motor starts.

Part III

Selecting Motor Drives

When you selected the speed of your motor, you had in mind how it would drive the equipment. Now you need to select the proper type and size of drive for the motor you have selected.

The type and size of drive you select are important for the following reasons: (1) these factors determine the speed at which your equipment runs, so the drive must be sized to fit your motor and your equipment; and (2) it must be strong enough to pull the load. Therefore, you have two decisions to make in selecting a drive:

A. What Type of Drive to Select.
B. What Size of Drive to Select.

A. What Type of Drive to Select

As you have already learned, the speed that your equipment runs, as compared to the speed of your motor, helps determine the type of drive you need. You may or may not be able to get a motor that turns at the same speed as that of your equipment. If not, you will have to provide a drive that will change the speed of your motor to the proper speed for your equipment.

From this discussion you will learn to recognize the different types of drives and how to select the right one for your job. The information you will need is given under the following headings:

1. Types of Drives.
2. Effect of Equipment Speed on Drive Selected.
3. Effect of Closeness of Motor to Equipment on Drive Selected.

1. TYPES OF DRIVES

You have two general types of drives from which to choose:

a. Direct Drive.
b. Speed Conversion Drive.

a. Direct Drives

Direct drives are for connecting a motor to equipment that runs at the same speed as the motor (Fig. 49). For example, if your equipment runs at 1725 rpm and your motor runs at the same speed, they can be connected directly to one another. The ones shown here provide flexing action which helps protect the motor bearings from wear caused by poor alignment of the shafts. They also protect the motor bearings from vibration developed by the equipment to which it is connected.

It is not likely that you will have to select a direct drive very often. Therefore, this discussion is limited to the four types most commonly used. They are as follows (Fig. 49):

(1) Flexible-Hose Coupling.
(2) Flange Coupling.
(3) Cushion-Flange Coupling.
(4) Flexible Shaft.

(1) **FLEXIBLE-HOSE COUPLING.** A flexible-hose coupling is made from a short section of ordinary plastic or

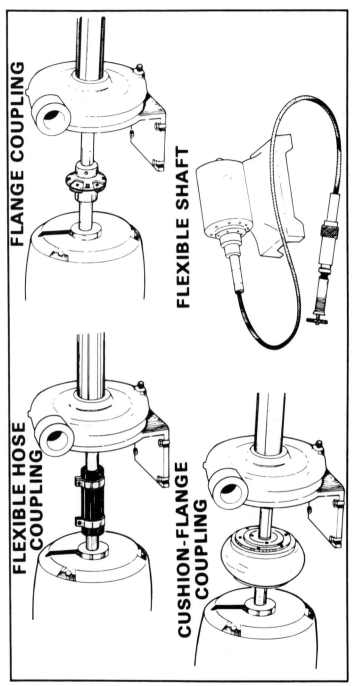

FLANGE COUPLING

FLEXIBLE SHAFT

FLEXIBLE HOSE COUPLING

CUSHION-FLANGE COUPLING

Fig. 49. Four of the more common types of direct drives used on electric motors. NOTE: Couplings must have guards before operation.

rubber hose (Fig. 49). It is easily installed. The ends of the hose are simply pushed over the ends of the motor and equipment shafts and clamped into position.

(2) FLANGE COUPLING. A flange coupling has half of the flanged coupling fastened to the motor shaft and the other half to the shaft of the equipment to be driven. The two halves are then fastened to a flexible disk which provides for flexing (Fig. 49).

Rigid-flange couplings are also available but they provide no flexing action. When this type is used, it is particularly important that the two shafts be in perfect alignment. That is, the end of the motor shaft and the end of the equipment shaft must be parallel with each other.

(3) CUSHION-FLANGE COUPLING. A cushion-flange coupling provides a tire-shaped segment to which the two flanges attach (Fig. 49). It is similar to the hose-type coupling, except that it is more durable, provides for more flexing action, and it comes in sizes for motors of larger horsepower.

(4) FLEXIBLE SHAFT. Direction of rotation is important when purchasing a flexible shaft. It must run in the direction for which it is built. If your equipment must turn in a certain direction, be sure to indicate whether it operates in a clockwise direction or a counterclockwise direction when placing an order for a flexible shaft.

b. Speed-Conversion Drive

A speed-conversion drive is used if your motor does not turn at the recommended speed of your equipment. You have a choice of three different speed-conversion drives. They are as follows (Fig. 50):

(1) Pulley-and-Belt Drive.
(2) Gear Drive (not discussed).
(3) Chain-and-Sprocket Drive (not discussed).

(1) PULLEY-AND-BELT DRIVE. Since the pulley-and-belt drive is the one you will most likely use, it is the only type of speed-conversion drive discussed here. The

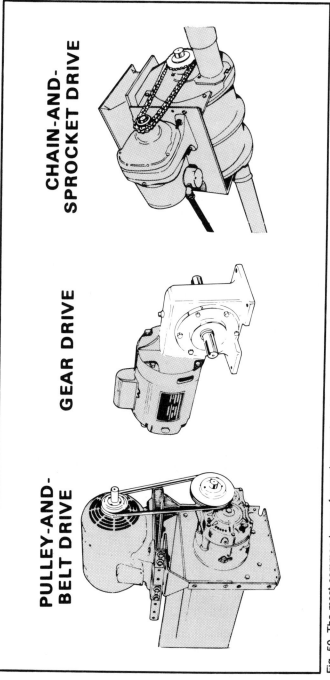

CHAIN-AND-SPROCKET DRIVE

GEAR DRIVE

PULLEY-AND-BELT DRIVE

Fig. 50. The most common types of speedconversion drives used with electric motors. Safety shields must be installed on belt and chain drives before operating.

reason: the selection of units that go into the gear drives and chain-and-sprocket drives involves considerable knowledge for application to various specialized needs. Consequently, the selection of these types of drive units is left to specialists and not discussed further in this book.

Pulley-and-belt drives consist of two pulleys or sheaves connected by a continuous belt loop (Fig. 50). One pulley is on the motor, and the other one is on the equipment.

NOTE: If your motor has a sleeve bearing, apply belt pull opposite the oil window in the sleeve for more bearing surface.

There are four types of pulley-and-belt drives (Fig. 51):

(a) V-Belt.
(b) Webbed Multi-V-Belt.
(c) Flat-Belt.
(d) V-Flat.

(a) V-Belt

A V-belt drive consists of two V-pulleys (often called sheaves), one on the motor and one on the driven equipment (Fig. 51). They are connected by a single V-belt, or by two or more V-belts, depending on the size of the load.

(b) Webbed Multi-V-Belt

The webbed multi-V-belt drive is a combination of two or more V-belts webbed together as one belt (Fig. 51). It has the advantages of using several single V-belts, and it prevents belt turnover and slipping problems that sometimes occur when two or more single V-belts are used. Special V-pulleys are available for use with this type of belt.

(c) Flat-Belt

A flat-belt drive is, as the name implies, a flat belt on two flat pulleys, one on the driven equipment and one on the motor (Fig. 51). A flat belt is not used unless the motor needs to be placed at a considerable distance from the equipment that is being driven. This may be the case where you wish to keep

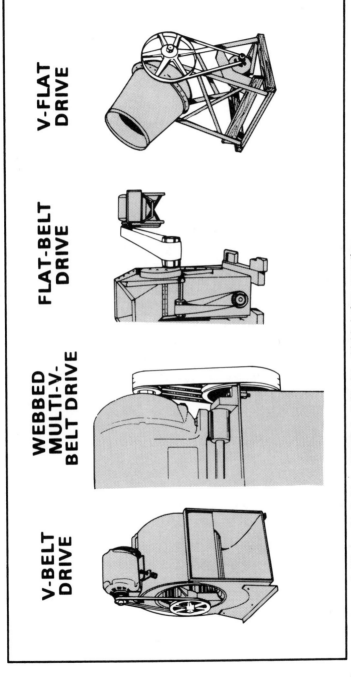

V-FLAT DRIVE

FLAT-BELT DRIVE

WEBBED MULTI-V-BELT DRIVE

V-BELT DRIVE

Fig. 51. Types of pulley-and-belt drives. NOTE: Install safety shields before operation.

a motor with an open or splash-proof enclosure out of very dusty conditions. Its use has been largely replaced, however, by totally-enclosed motors using V-belt drives. Because of this fact, flat belts are not discussed further in this book.

(d) V-Flat

A V-flat drive consists of a V-pulley on the motor and a flat pulley on the driven equipment (Fig. 51). A standard V-belt is used, one that fits the V-pulley on the motor.

The flat surface of the V-belt—the inner surface that rides on the flat pulley—is rather narrow. But it has so much contact area on the large flat pulley that there is usually no problem of having enough friction to avoid slippage.

2. EFFECT OF EQUIPMENT SPEED ON DRIVE SELECTED

If your equipment turns the same speed as the motor, a direct drive is usually recommended. The type of direct drive you use is not limited by the speed. You can use any one of four types previously described.

You can also use a pulley-and-belt drive without changing the speed of the equipment. To do this, use pulleys of the same size on the motor and equipment.

If the equipment must turn at a different speed from that of the motor, use a pulley-and-belt drive. You have a wide selection of pulley-and-belt drives which will enable you to secure any speed you wish for your equipment.

3. EFFECT OF CLOSENESS OF MOTOR TO EQUIPMENT ON DRIVE SELECTED

If your motor is to be mounted on, or near, the equipment, a direct drive is convenient—providing the operating speeds are the same.

If, for some reason, you need to install the motor a short distance away from your equipment, you can use a motor with an extended shaft to provide a direct drive, or you can use a pulley-and-belt drive.

With V-belts, the motor and equipment can be as far as 4 or 5 feet apart. With flat belts, the distance can be greater. Check with your local dealer because the motor size, equipment size, and the availability of different sizes of pulleys and belts can affect distance.

With V-flat belt drives, it is generally recommended that the distance from the center of the motor pulley to the center of the equipment pulley be no greater than the diameter of the equipment pulley. By mounting the motor this close to the driven pulley, you will have very little belt slippage on the flat pulley, because the belt(s) have a large area of contact on the flat pulley.

B. What Size of Drive to Select

Now that you know what type of drive you are going to use, you must determine the size needed. The size of the drive depends on the power to be delivered and the speed. If you get one that is too small for the power you are transmitting, it will not last long. Or, if you get the wrong size pulleys on a pulley-and-belt drive, the speed will be wrong.

Sizes of drives are expressed under the following headings:

1. How Sizes of Drives are Expressed.
2. Determining Size of Direct Drive Needed.
3. Determining Size of Pulley-and-Belt Drive Needed.

1. HOW SIZES OF DRIVES ARE EXPRESSED

The sizes of drives are expressed in different ways, depending on the type of drive. Direct drives are sized by power. Pulley-and-belt drives are sized by the diameter of the pulleys needed to get the right equipment speed and by the size and number of belts required to deliver the power.

The bore sizes of both drives (direct and pulley-and-belt) are determined by the shaft sizes of the motor and equipment (Fig. 52). Drives are either manufactured to fit the shaft directly or they are fitted with a bushing on the correct inside diameter to fit the shaft and the correct outside diameter to

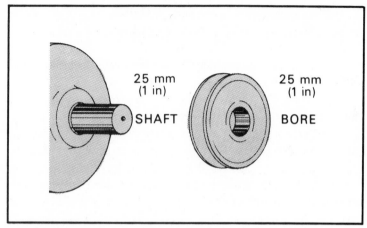

Fig. 52. When ordering a direct drive unit or a pulley, it is important that you give the bore size.

fit into the drive coupling or pulley. By having several sizes of bushings, one drive can be used on different-size shafts. Occasionally, this is an advantage if the same drive is to be used on different pieces of equipment or different sizes of motor shafts.

You will learn from the following discussion how to determine the sizes of both direct drives and pulley-and-belt drives. The information is given under the following headings:

2. DETERMINING SIZE OF DIRECT DRIVE NEEDED

If you decided on a direct drive for your job, be sure to get one that matches the horsepower that is being transmitted. If it is too small, it will not last long. If it is too big, it will cost more than necessary.

Sizes of direct drives are rated in horsepower. If your motor is .28 kW (1/3 hp) or less, you can use a flexible hose coupling (Fig. 49).

If your motor is .28 kW (1/3 hp) or more—up to almost any horsepower size—you can use either the flanged or cushioned type of coupling (Fig. 49).

If the motor is any size up to 1.6 kW (2 hp), you will have no trouble finding a flexible shaft of the proper size (Fig. 49).

3. DETERMINING SIZE OF PULLEY-AND-BELT DRIVE NEEDED

If you decided on a speed-conversion drive, it will most likely be a pulley-and-belt drive. For pulley-and-belt drives, you must know (1) what type and diameter of the pulleys to use, and (2) the type, number and length of belts to use.

It is important in your selection of pulley sizes that you make sure your equipment will run at its proper speed. Here are the reasons. When the operating speed is changed, the horsepower requirement on most equipment changes in the same proportion as the speed. For example, suppose a conveyor is operated by a .746 kW (1 hp) motor at a speed of 15.2 meters (50 ft.) per minute (Fig. 53). If the speed is increased to twice the speed (30.5 meters [100 ft.] per minute), the power requirement will increase by about twice as much. This will require a 1.5 kW (2 hp) motor (Fig. 53). If the speed is decreased by one-half the speed (7.6 meters [25 ft.] per minute), the power requirement will decrease about one-half. This will require a .4 kW (1/2 hp) motor (Fig. 53).

If your motor is driving a fan, blower, or centrifugal pump, and the speed is increased, the horsepower needed to operate it goes up very rapidly—by the cube of the increase in speed ratio. For example, a blower may operate satisfactorily at 400 rpm with a 2.5 kW (3 hp) motor. If the speed is doubled to 800 rpm, the speed ratio becomes 2, and $2 \times 2 \times 2 \times 2.5 = 20$ kW ($2 \times 2 \times 2 \times 3 = 24$ hp) is needed (Fig. 54).

To help you select the power size of pulley-and-belt drive, information is given under the following headings:

a. Determining the Type and Diameter of Pulleys Needed.
b. Determining the Type and Number of V-Belts Needed.
c. Determining the Length of V-Belt(s) Needed.
d. Factors Affecting Belt Life.

a. Determining the Type and Diameter of Pulleys Needed

Types and sizes of pulleys are discussed as follows:

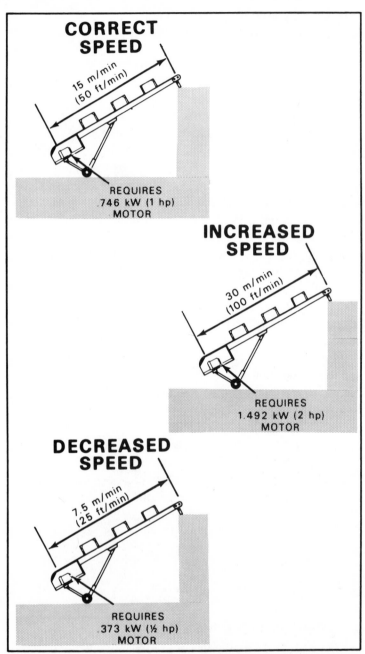

Fig. 53. Speed and power are important when selecting an electric motor for a job.

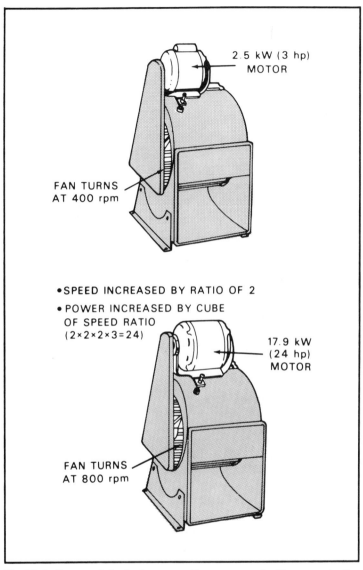

2.5 kW (3 hp)
MOTOR

FAN TURNS
AT 400 rpm

• SPEED INCREASED BY RATIO OF 2
• POWER INCREASED BY CUBE
OF SPEED RATIO
(2×2×2×3=24)

17.9 kW
(24 hp)
MOTOR

FAN TURNS
AT 800 rpm

Fig. 54. As the speed of a fan increases, the power required increases by the cube of the speed ratio.

(1) Type of Pulley.
(2) Diameter of Pulley.

(1) TYPE OF PULLEY. Most small motors used in

the home, shop and farm require only one V-belt. If that is what you need, you can select from three types of V-pulleys (Fig. 55):

(a) **Standard V-Pulley.** This should be your selection if the motor is to be used for only one job. It is the least expensive and is available in many sizes at most stores that sell pulleys.

(b) **V-Step Pulley.** This is the type to select if a variety of speeds is needed. It is very good for small, portable motors. Without changing pulleys, you can use the motor on different jobs that require different equipment speeds.

(c) **Adjustable V-Pulley** (Adjustable Sheave). One side of this type of pulley can be adjusted in or out to give more or less effective diameter. It is not as popular as the V-step pulley, partly because fewer outlets handle it and partly because it is more expensive. It is desirable if you need to have a very close adjustment on your equipment speed.

For larger-power uses where two or more belts are needed, use a standard V-pulley with as many grooves as you need.

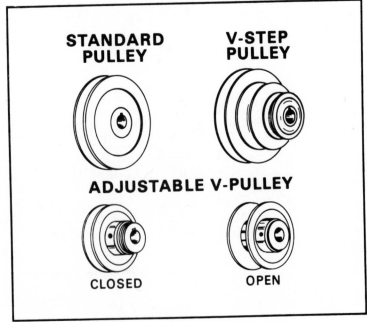

Fig. 55. Types of V-pulleys for single belt drives.

The number and size of grooves depend on the horsepower and the size of V-belts you use. This is discussed under the next heading.

The relative diameters of the pulleys are the size factors that determine the speed at which your equipment will run. You must select the pitch diameters that will change the speed of the motor to the correct operating speed of your equipment. The pitch diameter is the effective diameter at which the U-belt rides in the groove.

(2) DIAMETER OF PULLEY. Three methods are given here for determining the diameter sizes of pulleys:

(a) Pulley-Selection Chart.

(b) Pulley-Selection Formula.

(c) The Combination of Using Both the Chart and Formula with a Jackshaft.

(a) Pulley-Selection Chart. Use the pulley-selection chart in Fig. 56 if your equipment runs at 200 rpm or faster and your motor runs at 1725 rpm. Since 1725 rpm is standard speed for most motors, that is the only speed discussed here.

To use the pulley-selection chart (Fig. 56), proceed as follows:

1. *Select the left-hand column and proceed downward until you come to the size pulley you have or want on your motor.*

If your motor is less than .4 kW (1/2 hp), it is best that the motor pulley be not less than two inches in diameter for the least belt slippage. A smaller pulley may be used if your equipment is not operated often and if some belt slippage is not too important to the satisfactory operation of the equipment. If your motor is .4 kW (1/2 hp) or larger, it is best to use a motor pulley three inches or larger in diameter.

2. *Move across to the right until you come to a speed close to that of your machine.*

The white space shows how the chart works if your

Diameter of Pulley on Equipment—mm (in)

Diam. Motor Pulley mm(in)	Equipment Speed (RPM)														
	32 (1¼)	38 (1½)	45 (1¾)	51 (2)	58 (2¼)	64 (2½)	76 (3)	102 (4)	127 (5)	165 (6½)	203 (8)	254 (10)	306 (12)	381 (15)	457 (18)
32(1¼)	1725	1435	1230	1075	950	850	715	540	430	330	265	215	—	—	—
38(1½)	2075	1725	1475	1290	1140	1030	850	645	515	395	320	265	215	—	—
45(1¾)	2400	2000	1725	1500	1340	1200	1000	750	600	460	375	315	250	200	—
51(2)	2775	2290	1970	1725	1530	1375	1145	850	685	530	430	345	285	230	—
58(2¼)	3100	2580	2200	1930	1725	1550	1290	965	775	595	485	385	325	255	215
64(2½)	3450	2870	2460	2150	1900	1725	1435	1075	850	660	540	430	355	285	240
76(3)	4140	3450	2950	2580	2290	2070	1725	1290	1070	800	615	515	430	345	285
102(4)	5500	4575	3950	3450	3060	2775	2295	1725	1375	1060	860	700	575	460	375
127(5)	6850	5750	4920	4300	3825	3450	2865	2150	1725	1325	1075	860	715	575	475
165(6½)	8950	7475	6400	5600	4975	4480	3730	2790	2240	1725	1400	1120	930	745	620
203(8)	—	9200	7870	6900	6125	5520	4600	3450	2750	2120	1725	1375	1140	915	765
254(10)	—	—	9850	8620	7670	6900	5750	4300	3450	2650	2150	1725	1430	1140	950
302(12)	—	—	—	—	9200	8280	6900	5160	4130	3180	2580	2075	1725	1375	1140
381(15)	—	—	—	—	—	—	8635	6470	5170	3970	3230	2580	2150	1725	1425
457(18)	—	—	—	—	—	—	—	7750	6200	4770	3880	3100	2580	2070	1725

Fig. 56. Pulley-selection chart for motors turning 1725 rpm. Speeds shown are for the driven equipment in revolutions per minute.

motor is equipped with a 76 mm (3-inch) pulley and you have a piece of equipment that you want to operate at 2100 rpm. Select the speed of 2070 rpm, as this is the closest to 2100 rpm.

3. *Proceed upward to the pulley size for your equipment.*

A 64 mm (2 1/2 inch) pulley is needed for your equipment.

(b) Pulley-Selection Formula. Use the pulley-selection formula if your motor and equipment turn at different speeds from those given in the pulley-selection chart or if the pulley-selection chart is not available to you. It is given as follows:

$$\frac{\text{rpm of motor pulley} \times \text{Pitch Diameter of motor pulley}}{\text{rpm of equipment pulley} \times \text{Pitch Diameter of equipment pulley}}$$

Using the same example as in (a), to select the proper size pulleys by using the formula, proceed as follows:

1. *Choose the diameter of either the motor pulley or the equipment pulley.*

As in (a), select a 76 mm (3-inch) pulley for the motor.

2. *Find the diameter of the other pulley.*

Assume that the motor speed is 1725 rpm and the desired speed of the equipment is 2100 rpm.

SI: $1725 \times 76 = 2100 \times \text{diameter}$

$$\text{Diameter} = \frac{1725 \times 76}{2100}$$

Diameter = 62.4 mm
Use a 62 mm pulley

US: $1725 \times 3 = 2100 \times$ diameter

Dia. of equip. pulley $= \dfrac{1725 \times 3}{2100}$

Dia. of equip. pulley = 2.46 inches
Use a 2 1/2-inch pulley.

(c) The Combination of Using Both the Chart and Formula with a Jackshaft. If your equipment runs at a speed of less than 200 rpm (70 rpm for this example), you should use a jackshaft to help reduce the speed (Fig. 57). If the motor is .373 kW (1/2 hp) or less, the most practical arrangement is to use a 51 mm (2-inch) pulley on the motor to drive a 12-inch pulley on the jackshaft. (Larger motors require larger pulleys). To select the size of the second jackshaft pulley and the size of the pulley for the equipment, proceed as follows:

1. *Determine the speed of the first jackshaft pulley.*

   By using the table in Fig. 56, note that a 51mm (2 inch) motor pulley, turning at 1725 rpm, will cause a 305mm (12 inch) equipment pulley to turn at 285 rpm.

2. *Choose the diameter of the second jackshaft pulley.*

   For this example, use a 51 mm (2 inch) jackshaft pulley.

3. *Find the diameter of the equipment pulley.*

   By using the formula and substituting the second jackshaft pulley for the motor pulley.

   SI: $285 \times 51 = 70 \times$ diameter

   Diameter $= \dfrac{285 \times 51}{70}$

   Diameter = 207.6 mm
   Use a 208 mm pulley.

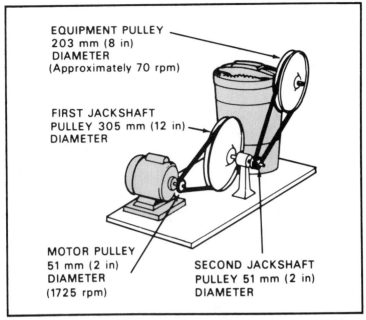

EQUIPMENT PULLEY
203 mm (8 in)
DIAMETER
(Approximately 70 rpm)

FIRST JACKSHAFT
PULLEY 305 mm (12 in)
DIAMETER

MOTOR PULLEY
51 mm (2 in)
DIAMETER
(1725 rpm)

SECOND JACKSHAFT
PULLEY 51 mm (2 in)
DIAMETER

Fig. 57. If your equipment operates at less than 200 rpm, use a jackshaft to help reduce the speed.

$$\text{US:} \quad 285 \times 2 = 70 \times \text{diameter}$$

$$\text{Dia. of equip. pulley} = \frac{285 \times 2}{70}$$

Dia. of equip. pulley = 8.14 inches
Use an 8-inch pulley.

b. Determining the Type and Number of V-Belts Needed

V-belts are classified according to their cross-sectional sizes. Also, you may find it advisable or necessary to use more than one V-belt. The number and type you use will be determined by the power required. Getting the proper size and number of belts is important. If they are too small, or too few in number, they will slip and wear out in a short time.

There are six standard types of V-belts: FP, A, B, C, D,

and E. Types FP, A, and B are most commonly used for power applications up to 5.6 kW (7 1/2 hp). They are shown in Fig. 58 along with the pulleys that are used with them.

(1) Fractional Power Belts. The fractional-power 3L belt is best for use with pulleys that are 635 mm (2 1/2 inches) and less in diameter. They are thin and much more flexible than types A-E.

(2) A-Section Belt. An A-section 4L belt is heavier. It can be used on small pulleys, but there is more slippage than with a thinner belt because the belt is too stiff to follow the pulling curvature. Instead, it arches out of the pulley groove and leaves only a small portion of the belt in the groove to do the pulley. It should not be used with a pulley smaller than three inches.

(3) B, C, D, and E Belts. The cross-sectional sizes increase with types, B, C, D, and E and should be used on larger pulleys.

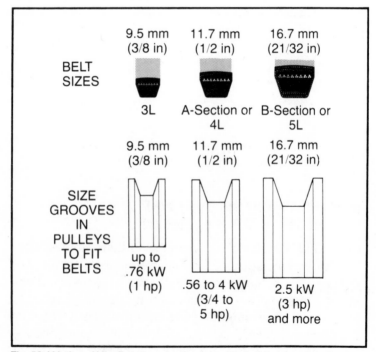

Fig. 58. V-belt and V-pulley sizes most commonly used for power applications up to 5.6 kW (7 1/2 hp).

Diam. of Motor Pulley mm(in)	Size of Motor							
	.4 (½ or Smaller)	.56 (¾)	.8 (1)	1.1 (1½)	1.5 (2)	2.5 (3)	4.0 (5)	5.6 kW (7½) hp
	Number and Type of Belt(s) Required							
51(2)	3L	3L						
63.5(2½)	3L	3L						
76(3)	1-A	1-A	1-A	2-A	2-A	3-A	5-A	8-A
89(3½)	1-A	1-A	1-A	2-A	2-A	3-A	4-A	7-A
102(4)	1-A	1-A	1-A	1-A	2-A	2-A	3-A	5-A
113.7(4½)	1-A	1-A	1-A	1-A	1-A	2-A	3-A	5-A
127(5)	1-A	-1-A	1-A	1-A	1-A	2-A	3-A	4-A
138.7(5½)	1-A	1-A	1-A	1-A	1-A	1-B	2-B	3-B
152(6)	1-A	1-A	1-A	1-A	1-A	1-B	2-B	2-B
178(7)	1-A	1-A	1-A	1-A	1-A	1-B	2-B	2-B
203(8)	1-A	1-A	1-A	1-A	1-A	1-B	1-B	2-B

Fig. 59. Number and type of V-belts and pulley sizes recommended for 1725 rpm motors of different powers.

The table shown in Fig. 59 gives the number and type of V-belt(s) you need for your particular pulley sizes and for your motor size. To make your selection, proceed as follows:

1. *Select the top column and proceed until you come to the size motor you have.*

For this example, use a 1.5 kW (2 hp) motor.

2. *Select the left-hand column and proceed downward until you come to the size pulley you have on your motor.*

For this example, use a 127 mm (5 inch) pulley.

3. *Move downward from the motor size and across from the pulley size.*

The white space shows your selection to be 1-A. This is one A-type belt.

The belt you select should have the same width of groove

as the pulley you are using (Fig. 58). This is particularly important if you want your equipment to operate at the speed you figured when you decided what pulley sizes to use. A V-belt will work in a wider pulley but it rides lower in the groove, giving the effect of a smaller pulley.

When a pulley and belt are properly matched, the top of the belt will fit flush with the edges of the pulley, unless an adjustable pulley is being used.

In purchasing a V-pulley you may notice that the outside diameter is larger than you asked for. This is because the pulley is rated by its effective diameter—the pitch diameter of the pulley where the V-belt rides. For example, the effective diameter on a pulley for an A-section belt is about 9.5 mm (3/8 inch) less than the outside diameter. For a B-section belt, it is about 11.7 mm (1/2 inch) less.

c. Determining the Length of V-Belt(s) Needed

To get the length of V-belt(s) you need, if the motor is already mounted, you have to measure it. There is not much you can do if the pulleys are too close for top efficiency. Use a tape and measure as shown in Fig. 60.

If your motor does not have to be mounted in a certain place on your equipment, the length belt you need is determined by the diameters of the pulleys and the distance between the motor and equipment shafts. The following procedure will give you the length of belt needed for an efficient operation.

Caution! Turn off power to motors with automatic switches such as air compressors.

Length of V-belt needed:

4 × diameter of largest pulley	_____
1.6 × diameter of motor pulley	_____
1.6 × diameter of equipment pulley	_____
Total length equals	_____

Where two or more single V-belts are used, they must be purchased as a set so that they will be exactly the same length and size. Otherwise, one of the belts will be carrying

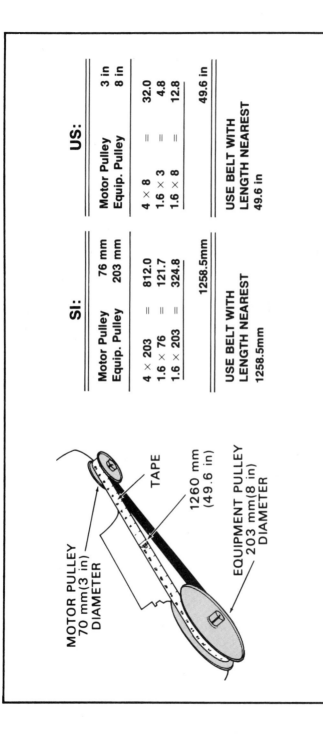

SI:

Motor Pulley	76 mm
Equip. Pulley	203 mm

4×203	=	812.0
1.6×76	=	121.7
1.6×203	=	324.8
		1258.5mm

**USE BELT WITH
LENGTH NEAREST
1258.5mm**

US:

Motor Pulley	3 in
Equip. Pulley	8 in

4×8	=	32.0
1.6×3	=	4.8
1.6×8	=	12.8
		49.6 in

**USE BELT WITH
LENGTH NEAREST
49.6 in**

MOTOR PULLEY
70 mm (3 in)
DIAMETER

TAPE

1260 mm
(49.6 in)

EQUIPMENT PULLEY
203 mm (8 in)
DIAMETER

Fig. 60. Methods of determining belt length. If your motor is already mounted on your equipment, measure as shown. If your motor can be placed at any distance from the equipment, compute the belt length, either method with SI or US.

most of the load and the other belt(s) will have a lot of slippage.

d. Factors Affecting Belt Life

You can extend the life of your belts by following some practical rules as follows:

1. *Keep pulleys aligned.*
2. *Adjust belt tension regularly and properly.*
3. *Keep belts clean and keep them free from oil and grease.*
4. *Use proper belts.*
5. *Never stretch belts over sheaves.*

Part IV

Servicing and Troubleshooting

Electric motors require very little maintenance—so little, in fact, that they are often neglected. Under normal operating conditions, motors should be serviced about once each year. When motors are operated under severe conditions such as hot, cold and dust, service the motors more often.

When trouble occurs, refer to the Troubleshooting Guides that follow. You will be able to correct most of the problems. If you are not skilled in the procedures for testing and repair, consult a qualified person.

Proceed as follows:

1. *Disconnect power from motor.*

   Caution! Never work on a motor without disconnecting the power; and make sure it cannot be turned on by someone else.

2. *Clean the motor.*

   Dust and dirt accumulation will cause overheating.

3. *Check bearings for wear.*

   Excessive end play will cause the motor to draw more starting current.

4. *Check shaft for freedom of rotation.*
5. *Lubricate according to manufacturer's recommendations.*

   Do not overlubricate.

6. *Check wiring.*

   Check for loose, frayed or bare wires.

7. *Clean starting switch contacts where applicable.*

   Split-phase and capacitor motors have contact points that should be cleaned with fine sandpaper. Do not use emery cloth. It tends to insulate the points.

8. *Check brushes on wound rotor motors.*
9. Clean brushes and commutator where applicable.

   Use fine sandpaper.

10. *Check drive mechanisms.*

    Check belts for condition and proper tension. Check pulleys for alignment.

Electric motors are noted for long life and few problems. You can extend the long life and reduce maintenance problems further by following a few simple rules:

- *Provide for optimum environment.*

  Dust, excessive heat, chemicals, and moisture are environmental conditions to avoid whenever possible.

- *Select the proper motor for the job.*

  Do not overload the motor.

- *Install the motor correctly.*

  Mount securely and align drives.

- *Provide for correct voltage.*

  Voltages that are either too high or too low can be

damaging to your motor. Three-phase voltages should be balanced. Provide adequate size feeder circuits with proper protection.

- *Maintain your motor properly.*

TROUBLE-SHOOTING GUIDE FOR ALL MOTORS

TROUBLE	Motor fails to start	Motors hums but will not start	Rotor must be shifted to start	Motor runs—then stops	Slow acceleration	Overheating	Excessive vibration	Low speed	What To Do
Probable Cause									
Open circuit	x	x							Check wiring—Check voltage
Defective motor windings	x								Inspect and repair
Starter switch doesn't close		x							Clean and lubricate, or replace
Bad capacitor		x		x	x				Check and replace
Open rotor or starter	x	x							Locate and replace

Overloaded		x	x	x	x	x	x	Lighter load
Low voltage		x	x	x	x	x	x	Lighter line load—Increase size of lead wire
Worn bearings		x		x	x			Replace
Lack of Lubrication		x	x	x	x			Lubricate
Defective overload protection				x				Locate and replace
Grounds or short circuits					x	x	x	Locate and repair
Wrong connections					x	x		Check wiring diagrams
Belt too tight					x	x		Slacken belt
Dirt, dust, trash					x	x		Clean
Unbalanced					x	x		Balance
Misalignment					x	x		Align
Loose mounting					x			Tighten
Poor connection	x	x						Inspect and connect

TROUBLE-SHOOTING GUIDE FOR WOUND ROTOR MOTORS
(Motors with Brushes)

Probable Cause	Motor fails to start	Slow acceleration	Low speed	Excessive sparking—starting	Excessive sparking—running	Rapid brush wear	Excessive speed	What To Do
Worn brushes	x	x		x				Replace brushes
Brushes stuck	x	x	x					Adjust brushes
Brushes not set	x	x	x					Check with marks on frame
Dirty commutator		x	x					Clean and sandpaper

114

Cause						Remedy
Rough commutator	x	x				Clean and sandpaper
High commutator bars	x		x			Turn in lathe
High mica	x		x			Undercut mica
Overloaded	x		x			Lighten load
High voltage			x			Check voltage
Low voltage	x		x			Check voltage
Governor stuck				x		Adjust governor
Governor out of adjustment				x		Adjust governor
Poor connections	x					Test and tighten
Commutator out of round	x					Turn in lathe
Dirty short circuiting device			x	x		Clean with solvent
Shorted rotor winding					x	Inspect and repair

Acknowledgments

Acknowledgment is given for the excellent suggestions, criticisms and assistance given by the following:

EDUCATION

Alberta
Douglas A. Taylor, Research and Development Coordinator, Alberta, Canada

Arizona
Clinton O. Jacobs, Professor, Agricultural Education, The University of Arizona

Iowa
Thomas A. Hoerner, Professor, Agricultural Engineering, The Iowa State University

Kansas
Ralph Lipper, Professor, Agricultural Engineering, Kansas State University

Damon E. Slyter, Agricultural Education Program Specialist, Kansas State Department of Education

North Carolina
C.V. Tart, Chief Consultant, Vocational Agricultural Education, North Carolina

Wisconsin
F.J. Doering, Head Consultant, Vocational Agricultural Education, Wisconsin

INDUSTRY

Baldor Electric Company
James Adams and **Damon Elkins,** Ft. Smith, AR 72901

Beckwith Electric Company, Inc.
Roger A. Smith, Marketing Service Manager, Largo, FL 33540

Bodine Electric Company
Christopher Bodine, Market Analyst, 2500 Bradley Place, Chicago, IL 60618

Central Power Systems, Inc.
Jack Lippincott, Manager, Box 657, Fulton, MO 65275

Cummings Georgia, Inc.
Larry Brock, 141 Brockwell Court, Atlanta, GA 30336

Dayton Electric Mfg. Co.
5959 W. Howard Street, Dept. R, Chicago, IL 60648

Fairbanks-Morse Power Division
Jamie Owen, Analyst-Order Application and **Gene Strautman,** National Account Manager, 3601 Fairbanks Avenue, Kansas City, KS 66110

Georgia Power Company
Olin W. Ginn, Manager, Agribusiness Development Department, Atlanta, GA 30336

General Electric Corporation
Dominic L. Bosa, Product Development, Bldg. 16, Room 241, Schenectady, NY 12345

Gould, Inc., Electric Motor Division
L.A. Will, Marketing Services, St. Louis, MO 63166

Louis Allis-Litton
Gerald Calvert, Products Manager, NEMA Frame Motors, 427 E. Stewart Street, Milwaukee, WI 53201

Reliance Electric Company
Chester J. Cobosco, Motor Engineer and **Joseph H. Pontzer,** Mechanical Engineering Mgr., Collins Industrial Blvd., Athens, GA 30613

Ronk Electrical Industries, Inc.
Ivan Winsett, Manufacturing Representative, Nokomis, IL

Universal Electric
Kathryne A. Snell, Director of Public Relations, 300 E. Main Street, Owosso, MI 48867

U.S. Electrical Motors
Z.G. Brandenstein, Manager of Sales and Training, 125 Old Gate Lane, Milford, CT 06460

Westinghouse Electric Corporation
R.E. Manville, Coordinator, Market Planning and Services, Motor Division, P.O. Box 22FTR, Buffalo, NY 14240

OTHERS

National Electric Manufacturers Association
2101 L St. N.W., Washington, DC 20037

National Fire Protection Association
Battery March Park, Quincy, MA 02269

References

Agricultural Wiring Handbook, Farm Electrification Council, Columbia, MO.

AC Motors—Insulation, Enclosures and Service Factor, Westinghouse Electric Corporation, Buffalo, NY.

The Design, Application Benefits and Economics of Energy-Efficient Motors, **Donald R. Aldworth,** Gould, Inc., AIPE Journal, Fall 1981.

Effect of Motor Efficiency on Energy Savings, **Donald Aldworth,** Gould, Inc., Electrical Construction and Maintenance, September 1981.

Electric Motors Save Energy, Cut Cost, **Daniel V. Elson,** Associate Editor, Design News, August 6, 1979.

Energy Saving Electric Motors, Federal Energy Administration, August 1977.

F.H.P. Motor Terminology, Bodine Electric Co.

Fundamentals of Electricity for Agriculture, **Robert J. Gustafson,** AVI Publishing Co., Inc., 1980.

General Installation, Operation and Maintenance Instruction, Gould, Inc., 1978.

Gentlemen, Change Your Motors, **Clarence E. Wise,** Staff Editor, Machine Design, August 1979.

Induction Motors 1-200 HP, Lesson No. B-13, Product Training Program, U.S. Motors.

Motor Control Circuit Design and the 1981 Code, **J.F. McPartland,** Editorial Director, EC&M, January 1981.

Motor Fundamentals, Lesson No. B-10, Product Training Program, U.S. Motors.

National Electrical Code, National Fire Protection Association, 1981.

V-Belt Drive Systems—Installation, Maintenance, Troubleshooting Guide, Dayton Electric Mfg. Co., Chicago, IL, May 1980.

Why Motors Fail, **Richard Scheinert,** Motor Facts, EC&M.

Index

Index

Other Bestsellers From TAB

Other Bestsellers From TAB